C0-AWZ-059

Oakland Community College
Orchard Ridge Campus Library
27055 Orchard Lake Road
Farmington Hills, MI 48018

NEGRO SONGS
FROM ALABAMA

NEGRO SONGS
FROM ALABAMA

Collected by Harold Courlander

Music transcribed by
John Benson Brooks

Revised and Enlarged
Second Edition

Published with the assistance of
The Wenner-Gren Foundation for Anthropological Research

OAK PUBLICATIONS   NEW YORK, N.Y.

M
1670
.C75
N4
1963
OR   5/88

Photographs by Harold Courlander
Cover Design by Ronald Clyne

First edition © 1960 by Harold Courlander
This edition, revised and enlarged, © 1963 by Harold Courlander

CONTENTS

INTRODUCTION

ASPECTS OF U.S. NEGRO FOLK MUSIC

I.   RELIGIOUS SONGS: PRAYERS, ANTHEMS
                       AND SPIRITUALS

   1. MOVE MEMBERS MOVE
      Rosie Hibler and family, Marian,
      Mississippi

   2. DIDN'T YOU HEAR
      Rich Amerson and Earthy Anne Coleman,
      Livingston, Alabama

   3. WAKE UP JONAH
      Rich Amerson and Earthy Anne Coleman,
      Livingston, Alabama

   4. ROCK CHARIOT
      Rich Amerson, Earthy Anne Coleman and
      Price Coleman, Livingston, Alabama

   5. PREACH MY GOSPEL
      Annie Grace Horn Dodson, Livingston,
      Alabama

   6. WHEN YOU FEEL LIKE MOANING
      Rich Amerson, Livingston, Alabama

   7. JOB, JOB
      Rich Amerson and Earthy Anne Coleman,
      Livingston, Alabama

   8. PRAYER
      Dock Reed and Vera Hall Ward,
      Tuscaloosa, Alabama

   9. THE SUN WILL NEVER GO DOWN
      Dock Reed, Livingston, Alabama

  10. THIS MAY BE YOUR LAST TIME
      Rich Amerson and Earthy Anne Coleman,
      Livingston, Alabama

  11. KING DAVID
      Rich Amerson and Earthy Anne Coleman,
      Livingston, Alabama

  12. IT'S GETTING LATE IN THE EVENING
      Rich Amerson and Earthy Anne Coleman,
      Livingston, Alabama

  13. TRAVELLING SHOES
      Vera Hall Ward, Tuscaloosa, Alabama

  14. WONDER WHERE IS MY BROTHER GONE
      Annie Grace Horn Dodson, Livingston,
      Alabama

  15. DEATH IS AWFUL
      Dock Reed and Vera Hall Ward,
      Tuscaloosa, Alabama

  16. TROUBLED, LORD, I'M TROUBLED
      Dock Reed and Vera Hall Ward,
      Tuscaloosa, Alabama

  17. TRAMPING, TRAMPING
      Dock Reed, Livingston, Alabama

  18. DEAR AND GONE
      Dock Reed and Vera Hall Ward,
      Tuscaloosa, Alabama

  19. FREE AT LAST
      Dock Reed and Vera Hall Ward,
      Tuscaloosa, Alabama

  20. I'M GOING HOME ON THE MORNING
      TRAIN
      Dock Reed, Livingston, Alabama

  21. JESUS GOING TO MAKE UP MY DYING
      BED
      Dock Reed, Livingston, Alabama

  22. OH DEATH HAVE MERCY
      Rich Amerson and Earthy Anne Coleman,
      Livingston, Alabama

  23. COME ON UP TO BRIGHT GLORY
      Rich Amerson and Earthy Anne Coleman,
      Livingston, Alabama

  24. I'M CLIMBING UP THE HILLS OF
      MT. ZION
      Dock Reed and Vera Hall Ward,
      Tuscaloosa, Alabama

  25. PLUMB THE LINE
      Dock Reed and Vera Hall Ward,
      Tuscaloosa, Alabama

  26. GOING TO SHOUT ALL OVER GOD'S
      HEAVEN
      Dock Reed and Vera Hall Ward,
      Tuscaloosa, Alabama

  27. LORD, I'M WAITING ON YOU
      Rich Amerson and Earthy Anne Coleman,
      Livingston, Alabama

  28. TIP AROUND MY BED RIGHT EASY
      Dock Reed, Livingston, Alabama

  29. LOOK HOW THEY DONE MY LORD
      Vera Hall Ward and Dock Reed,
      Tuscaloosa, Alabama

  30. MY GOD AINT NO LYING MAN
      Dock Reed and Vera Hall Ward,
      Tuscaloosa, Alabama

  31. WHEN THE ROLL IS CALLED IN HEAVEN
      Franklin Speed, Willie Henry Willis, Jr.,
      Joe Brown, Harrison Ross, and Willie
      John Strong, Livingston, Alabama

  32. I'M STANDING IN A SAFETY ZONE
      Rosie N. Winston, Livingston, Alabama

II. WORK AND FIELD SONGS

  33. JOHN HENRY
      Rich Amerson, Livingston, Alabama

  34. BLACK WOMAN
      Rich Amerson, Livingston, Alabama

  35. WATER ON THE WHEEL
      Annie Grace Horn Dodson, Livingston,
      Alabama

36. CAPTAIN HOLLER HURRY
Willie Turner, Livingston, Alabama

37. THE CAPTAIN CAN'T READ
Rich Amerson, Livingston, Alabama

38. NOW YOUR MAN DONE GONE
Willie Turner, Livingston, Alabama

39. SHE DONE GOT UGLY
Archie Lee Hill, Livingston, Alabama

40. EVALINA
Rich Amerson, Livingston, Alabama

41. I'M GOING UPTOWN
Emmanuel Jones, Livingston, Alabama

III. CALLS, CRIES AND HOLLERS

42. HEY RUFUS
Annie Grace Horn Dodson, Livingston, Alabama

43. WOH HOO (field call)
Annie Grace Horn Dodson, Livingston, Alabama

44. I'M GOING DOWN THE ROAD
Enoch Brown, Livingston, Alabama

45. FATHER'S FIELD CALL
Annie Grace Horn Dodson, Livingston, Alabama

46. CHILDREN'S FIELD CALL
Annie Grace Horn Dodson, Livingston, Alabama

IV. LULLABIES

47. GIVE MY HEART EASE
Earthy Anne Coleman, Livingston, Alabama

48. LITTLE LAP DOG
Vera Hall Ward, Tuscaloosa, Alabama

V. CHILDREN'S GAME SONGS

49. LOOP DE LOO
Children of Lilly's Chapel School, York, Alabama

50. MARY MACK
Children of Lilly's Chapel School, York, Alabama

51. KUSHIE DYE YO
Celina Lewis, Livingston, Alabama

52. MAY GO ROUND THE NEEDLE
Children of East York School, East York, Alabama

53. AMASEE
Children of Brown's Chapel School, Livingston, Alabama

54. ROSIE DARLING ROSIE
Children of Brown's Chapel School, Livingston, Alabama

55. GREEN GREEN ROCKY ROAD
Children of Lilly's Chapel School, York, Alabama

56. JUST WATCH THAT LADY
Children of Lilly's Chapel School, York, Alabama

57. SANGAREE
Celina Lewis, Livingston, Alabama

58. PEEP SQUIRREL
Celina Lewis, Livingston, Alabama

59. CHARLIE OVER THE OCEAN
Children of East York School, East York, Alabama

60. SEE SEE RIDER
Children of Lilly's Chapel School, York, Alabama

61. BLUEBIRD BLUEBIRD
Children of Pilgrim Church School, Livingston, Alabama

62. GOING UP NORTH
Children of East York School, East York, Alabama

63. LITTLE SALLY WALKER
Children of Lilly's Chapel School, York, Alabama

64. OLD LADY SALLY WANTS TO JUMP
Children of Lilly's Chapel School, York, Alabama

65. STOOPING ON THE WINDOW
Children of East York School, East York, Alabama

66. BOB-A-NEEDLE
Children of Lilly's Chapel School, York, Alabama

67. ROSIE GAL
Celina Lewis, Livingston, Alabama

INTRODUCTION

The folk songs and tunes in this collection were recorded in Alabama and Mississippi in 1950. Out of several hundred recordings, eighty-four were published on pressings by the Ethnic Folkways Library in a six-album series entitled "Negro Folk Music of Alabama." Transcriptions of these eighty-four tunes were made by John Benson Brooks, and sixty-seven of them were selected for inclusion in this book. Some others which are not in this collection are to be found in my book, Negro Folk Music in the United States, published by Columbia University Press.

Apart from the usual motive of looking for songs that are not commonplace in the available literature, there were two conscious objectives in the 1950 field recording project. One was to document Negro musical activities in a limited region to get a notion of their extent and nature. Another was to investigate the manner in which Negro folk songs are really sung in their natural setting.

The difference between living Negro folk music and the available printed representations of such music is considerable. Our attitude toward music is strongly oriented toward neat form. Our notations of folk music have all too often tried to adjust irregularities so that the songs appear in tidy packages. In effect this has meant tampering with melodic lines and with the musical phrasing, and laying out the measures "just so." However, much of Negro folk music cannot be compressed into forms that are the result of convention and preconception without destroying much of its special qualities.

Written music is limited in its ability to represent what is heard. But in transcribing these songs, John Benson Brooks has undertaken to convey as nearly as possible what is actually taking place musically -- that is, to treat the materials, where appropriate, as though composed rather than strophic. Thus, in many instances there are no neat stanzas or repetitions of clearly defined phrasing. It is evident that the singers often "play around" with basic melodies, developing ornamentations and effects that are pleasing to them. Word sounds frequently are altered, abbreviated, or drawn out to achieve these effects. Never subjected to the discipline of written music, the singers rarely present a piece twice in exactly

the same way. Much depends on the mood, the circumstances, and the responsive voice or voices. It is clear that while the singers have basic concepts of form, melodic line, and what is harmonically permissible, these elements are subject to artistic, playful, or emotionally meaningful alteration.

Some familiar types and categories of Negro songs are not represented here -- the traditional blues, for example. Although a large number of blues were recorded, many of them seemed to be familiar and derivative of early performers or phonograph discs. It was felt that it would be wasteful of space to displace some other choices to make room for them. However, this book does contain examples of atypical blues forms (such as "Black Woman" and "I'm Going Uptown"). In addition, there are work songs, lullabies, children's play songs, various types of field calls and cries, a large and diverse body of religious songs, prayers, examples of rocking and reeling songs, moaning, an old hymn that has undergone a remarkable transfiguration, and a version of "John Henry" that is a free and true ballad.

Throughout the 1950 recording trip I had the invaluable assistance of my wife, Emma Courlander; and while in the Livingston, Alabama, area Mrs. Ruby Tartt was exceedingly helpful in directing me to a number of singers, including Rich Amerson, Dock Reed, Vera Hall Ward, and Annie Grace Horn Dodson. Others who were most helpful were the late Thomas M. Campbell, at Tuskeegee; S. W. Boynton, Dallas County Agriculture Agent at Selma; Rebecca Anderson and the Reverend E. D. Tuckey of the Shiloh Primitive Baptist Church at Bogue Chita; Mr. C. J. Hurston, Principal of the Dallas County Training School; teachers of the various country schools where children's songs were recorded; and the singers themselves, whose names are noted in the table of contents. There were, of course, many other singers whose songs and names do not appear here. Grants from the Wenner-Gren Foundation for Anthropological Research assisted in the collection, transcribing, and original publication of this material.

Harold Courlander

Bethesda, Maryland, 1962

ASPECTS OF U.S. NEGRO FOLK MUSIC

So much has been said about Negro folk music in the United States during the past half century or so that one may well wonder whether anything useful can be added. But there are good reasons to reexamine the substance of Negro folk music. For one thing, studies in anthropology and ethnomusicology have given us a larger view of this subject than we once had. For another, genuine folk music in the United States has been all but submerged in a sea of arrangements, popularizations, and inept imitations of the originals. We have almost forgotten what Negro religious songs, for example, sounded like in a homogeneous setting only a few years ago. Many of those songs have been interpolated, rearranged, mangled, and debased in the repertoires of choral groups, folk music performers, jazz groups, and popular singers. Worksongs and old field blues have become raw material for experimentation and sensation-provoking pop songs. Furthermore, the tendency of the jazz world to appropriate Negro folk music for its own has blurred out some realistic distinctions between genuine folk music and the jazz genre. While there are those who maintain that jazz is the folk music of the atomic age, it is difficult indeed to come to any other conclusion but that it is a highly specialized popular art form that draws heavily upon folk music.

It will not be possible in the short space permitted here to more than touch upon some of the aspects of Negro folk music -- mainly its origin, development, and relationships, its musical characteristics, and its literary and social content.

The confrontation of African and European musical cultures in the New World during colonial days could have had only one result -- acculturation. African concepts of musical form were juxtaposed with European musical forms, and each drew substance and inspiration from the other. The first Africans in the United States undoubtedly sang songs and played instruments familiar in their homelands (ranging from Northwest Africa to the Congo). Descriptions of Negro musical performances of less than a century ago in Louisiana, and perhaps less than a half century ago in the Georgia Sea Islands, are all we need to be sure that African motifs and concepts persisted tenaciously through the years. Until very recent days, indeed, some music and dance activities in southern United States, such as the ring shout, testified to the sticking power of African tradition.

Nevertheless, the absorption into "Negro music" of European elements must have begun at a very early date. In her book Journal of a Residence on a Georgia Plantation, describing life in the 1830s, Frances Anne Kemble quoted some songs sung by slaves which (though she believed them to be of Negro invention) were of English derivation. Indeed, there are word elements in a vast number of quite old Negro songs that came originally from English folk songs, hymns,

and balladry. In French-speaking Louisiana, French tunes and word texts were absorbed in the same manner.

What we now know as "Negro folk music" is a result of adaptation and blending, of interpolation, of useful selection, and the continuing unconscious process of acculturation. It is a distinctive idiom, both musically and in its imagery. Sometimes it reveals startlingly its debt to European tradition; and sometimes its persistent non-European traits are conspicuous.

The United States was not the only place in the New World where the process of mixing and blending was going on. There were large concentrations of African slaves in the West Indies, in Brazil, and elsewhere. In Cuba, African musical idiom and Spanish musical idiom confronted each other. In Haiti, French and African. In Jamaica, English and African. In Brazil, Portuguese and African. Where the Negro population was large, and where social conditions favored preservation of indigenous ways, African elements in folk music remained strong until recent times. In Haiti, for example, even though French musical influence has been powerful, traditional music has a preponderant African flavor. In Jamaica African elements persist, though there has been a considerable blanching out effect.

What is noteworthy, among other things, is that there are still strong ties between American Negro folk music and the traditional music of the Caribbean, particularly that of the English speaking islands. Religious songs of the Bahamas, Trinidad, and Jamaica are closely akin to similar songs in Negro communities in the United States, and in many kinds of secular songs the similarities are remarkable. West Indian gang songs are closely related to our own Negro worksongs. And West Indian calypsos and our own blues have developed out of a common African song type -- the song of allusion, criticism, or complaint.

American Negro folk music has special characteristics of its own -- what it sounds like in terms of tones, intervals, rhythms, harmonies, and decorative elements. It is also distinctive, generally speaking, in the manner in which effects are achieved -- the use of the voice, the exploitation of instruments, and the events to which it is related. It uses various so-called gapped scales, such as the pentatonic, or the pentatonic with an additional note (often the major fourth or the major seventh). Other scales used include the major with a flatted seventh, the minor with a raised sixth, the minor without the sixth, and the minor with a raised seventh. Beyond these, there are many variations, some shared with other traditional music in the United States. Many traits of the scales used are encountered in European as well as in African music, so that it is not easy to determine primary influences.

Harmony is known and used in African singing, so that we cannot assume that harmonic elements are derived exclusively from European practice. In U.S. Negro usage, there are frequent simultaneous seconds, thirds, fourths, fifths, and octaves. The call and response type of singing is commonplace in religious songs, worksongs, children's game songs, and others, and one of its characteristics is the overlap of the parts -- that is, the responsive voice's tendency to come in before the initial voice has quite finished.

As for voice, there is frequent use of falsetto breaks, and "sweetness" is less of an objective than are throaty effects, some of which have what might be called a gravelly character.

The "blue" notes that have been given so much attention in literature on jazz are characteristic of many different genres of Negro folk music -- spirituals, worksongs, blues, etc.

Negro folk music in its natural setting has an intimate relationship to life. Work songs, for example, are tied in closely with work activities, and if sung elsewhere they lack their original significance. Work songs set the pace and rhythm of labor activity, and stimulate the participants. Blues songs, as we have already noted, are basically songs of complaint, criticism, or recrimination. They are meant to convey a message. When a blues song is transplanted into a strictly entertainment environment it has lost much of its significance.

One of the aspects of Negro religious songs that has not been given enough recognition is that they constitute a vast oral classical literature. Virtually every significant portion of the Bible is represented among the religious songs, starting with Adam and Eve and ending with the Revelations of St. John the Divine. Some religious songs have word texts lifted bodily out of the Bible. Others use a Biblical scene as a core and build around it a drama with bold imagery. Still others interpolate freely from any number of scenes, and a number of them, in complete form, approximate what we might call religious epics. Apart from all these, numerous spirituals and gospel songs, while making only slight (or even no) reference to Biblical texts, deal with questions of ethical and moral behavior. They may remind listeners that only the sanctified can cross the Jordan or that corn liquor is the road to ruination, or even tell people to keep their rockets off the moon.

1. MOVE MEMBERS MOVE

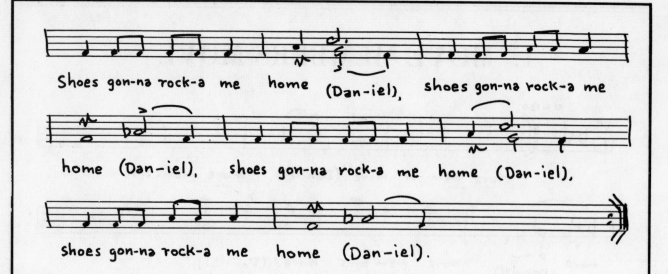

Shoes gon-na rock-a me home (Dan-iel), shoes gon-na rock-a me

home (Dan-iel), shoes gon-na rock-a me home (Dan-iel),

shoes gon-na rock-a me home (Dan-iel).

Then:

Move members move!
Move members move Daniel!   (3)
Who want to buy this land Daniel?   (6)
Who want to buy this land?
Who want to buy this land Daniel? } 3
Move members move Daniel!   (2)
Move till I get { there home Daniel!   (2)
Move till I get there Daniel!   (2)
Move till I get home Daniel!   (4)
Got on my little John shoes!
Got on my little John shoes Daniel! } 2
Shoes gonna rocka me home Daniel!   (6)

2. DIDN'T YOU HEAR

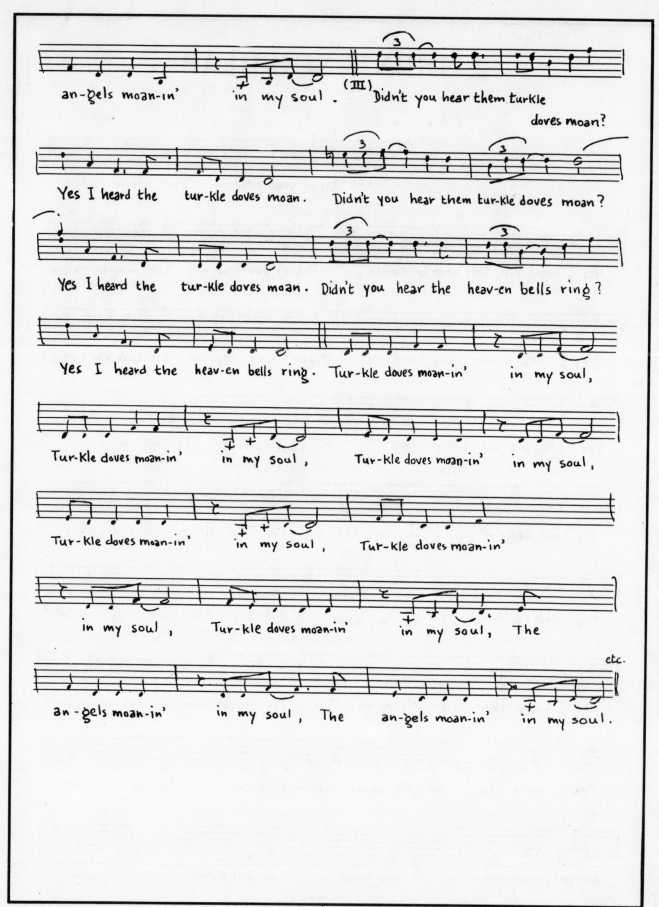

an-gels moan-in'   in my soul . (III) Didn't you hear them turkle
doves moan?

Yes I heard the   tur-kle doves moan.   Didn't you hear them tur-kle doves moan?

Yes I heard the   tur-kle doves moan. Didn't you hear the heav-en bells ring?

Yes I heard the   heav-en bells ring. Tur-kle doves moan-in'   in my soul,

Tur-kle doves moan-in'   in my soul ,   Tur-kle doves moan-in'   in my soul,

Tur-kle doves moan-in'   in my soul ,   Tur-kle doves moan-in'

in my soul ,   Tur-kle doves moan-in'   in my soul,   The

etc.

an-gels moan-in'   in my soul , The   an-gels moan-in' in my soul.

Then:

IV

Didn't you hear them harp when it blowed?
Yes I heard the harp when it blowed.
Didn't you hear them ravens cryin'?
Yes I heard the raven cryin'.
Didn't you hear that horn when it blowed?
Yes I heard the horn when it blowed.
Didn't you hear my Lord callin'?
Yes I hear my Lord call.
The turtle-dove moanin' my soul, (4)
The harp is blowin' my soul, (2)
My Lord callin' my soul. (2)

V

Didn't you hear that thunder roll?
Yes I heard the thunder roll.
Didn't you see the lightnin' flashin'?
Yes I see the lightnin' flash.
Didn't you hear them saints when they
    singin'?
Yes I hear the saints when they sing.
Didn't you hear that brother pray?
Yes I hear the brother pray.
Couldn't you hear them sisters shoutin'?
Yes I heard the sisters shout.
Didn't you hear them preachers preachin'?
Yes I heard the preachers preach.
Preachers preachin' my soul, (2)
Sisters shoutin' my soul, (2)
Thunder rollin' my soul. (2)

VI

Didn't you hear them organ playin'?
Yes I heard the organ playin'.
Didn't you hear them horns blowin'?
Yes I heard the horn when it blowed.
Didn't you hear them saints singin'?
Yes I heard the saints all singin'.
Saints all singin' my soul. (2)

3. WAKE UP JONAH

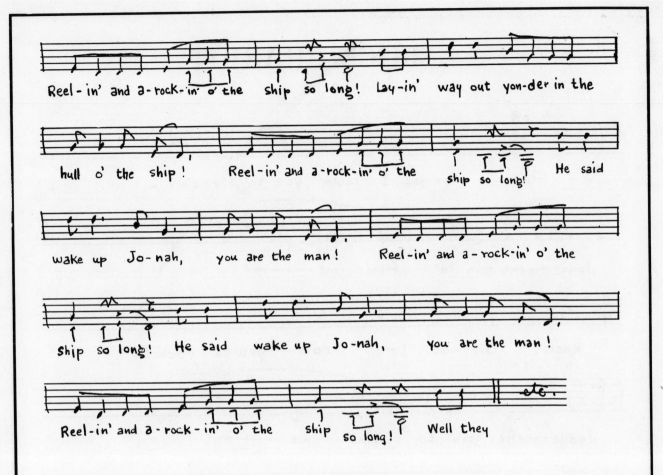

Reel-in' and a-rock-in' o' the ship so long! Lay-in' way out yon-der in the hull o' the ship! Reel-in' and a-rock-in' o' the ship so long! He said wake up Jo-nah, you are the man! Reel-in' and a-rock-in' o' the ship so long! He said wake up Jo-nah, you are the man! Reel-in' and a-rock-in' o' the ship so long! Well they

Then:

> Well they caught brother Jonah by hands
> and feet!
> Reelin' . . . . .
> Well they pitched brother Jonah up
> overboard!
> Reelin' . . . . .
> Well the water whale came along
> swallowed him whole!
> Reelin' . . . . .
> Then he puked brother Jonah on dry
> land!
> Reelin' . . . . .
> Then the gourd vine growed over Jonah's
> head!
> Reelin' . . . . .
> Then the inch worm come along cut it
> down!
> Reelin' . . . . .
> That made a cross over Jonah's head!
> Reelin' . . . . .

4. ROCK CHARIOT

Won't you rock, chariot,
    in the middle of the air? } 2
Judgement goin' to find me!
I wonder what chariot,
    comin' after me? } 2
Judgement goin' to find me!
Rock, chariot, I told you to rock!
Judgement goin' to find me! } 2
Elija' chariot, comin' after me!
Judgement ..... } 2
Rock, chariot, I told you to rock!
Judgement ..... } 2
Rock chariot, in the middle of the air!
Judgement ..... } 2
Wouldn't give you my shoes for
    your shoes!
Judgement ..... } 2
Wouldn't give you my robe for
    your robe!
Judgement ..... } 2
Wouldn't give you my crown for
    your crown!
Judgement ..... } 2
Wouldn't swap my soul for your soul!
Judgement ..... } 2
Rock, chariot, I told you to rock!
Judgement ..... } 2
Will you rock, chariot,
    in the middle of the air?
Judgement ..... } 2
Rock, chariot, in the middle of the air!
Judgement ..... } 2
Wouldn't give you my wings for
    your wings!
Judgement ..... } 2

Wouldn't swap you my grave for
    your grave!
Judgement ..... } 2
Rock, chariot, I told you to rock!
Judgement ..... } 2
Rock, chariot, in the middle of the air!
Judgement ..... } 2
I wonder what chariot,
    comin' after me!
Judgement ..... } 2
Elija' chariot, comin' after me!
Judgement ... } 2
That must be that gospel wheel!
Judgement ... } 2
What wheel children is you talkin' about?
Judgement ... } 2
Talkin' 'bout the wheel in Jesus Christ!
Judgement ... } 2
Every spoke is a human cry!
Judgement ... } 2
Ain't you talkin about the little wheel running
    in the wheel?
Judgement ... } 2
Them folks in Jesus Christ!
Judgement ... } 2
Wouldn't swap my wheel for your wheel!
Judgement ... } 2
Wouldn't give you my Lord for your Lord!
Judgment ... } 2
Ain't you got on them gospel shoes?
Judgement ... } 2
I wouldn't swap my shoes for your shoes!
Judgement ... } 2
I wouldn't give you my harp for your harp!
Judgement ... } 2

5. PREACH MY GOSPEL

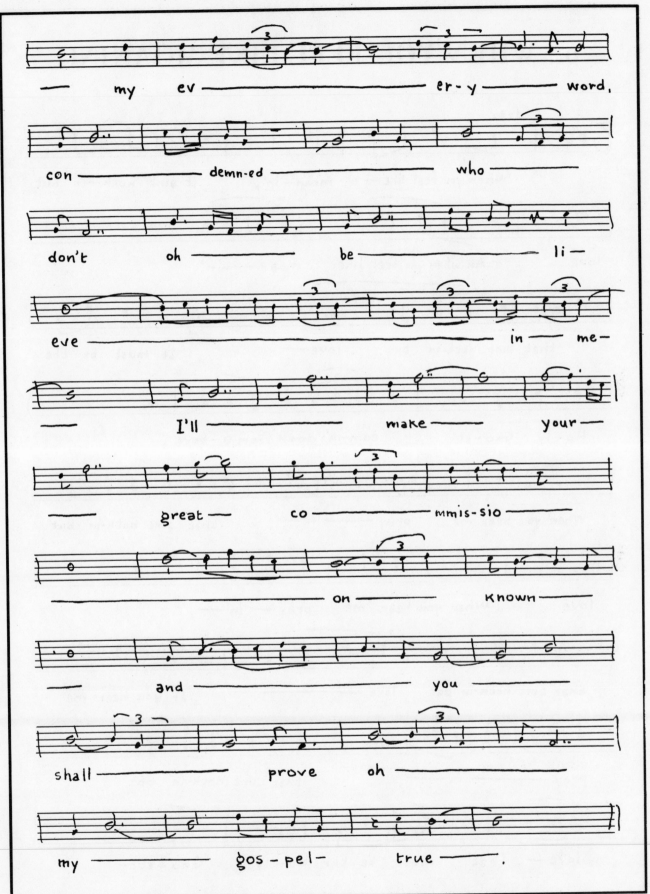

my ev — — — — — er-y — word,

con — — — demn-ed — — — who —

don't   oh — — be — — li —

eve — — — — in — me —

— I'll — — make — your —

— great — co — — mmis-sio

on — — — known

— and — — — you —

shall — — prove oh — — — —

my — — — gos-pel— true — .

6. WHEN YOU FEEL LIKE MOANING

com-in' down from a—bove. Do you love ev-ery-bo——dy—, taint noth-in' but love. When you love ev-ery bod————————y—, taint noth-in' but love————. When you love ev-ery—bo——dy—, taint noth-in' but love—. That must be the Ho——ly Ghost—— com-in' down from a—bove.

Then:

When you feel like groanin',
It ain't nothin' but love.   } 3
Children, that must be the Holy Ghost
Comin' down from above.
Do you love your preacher,
Taint nothin' but love.
When you love your preacher,   } 2
It ain't nothin' but love.
That must be the Holy Ghost
Comin' down from above.

7. JOB, JOB

—on, oh— Rock Mount Zi——on in that mor——

ning. Don't you hear the train— com-in'———, hear the

train— com-in'———, don't you hear the train——

com—in' in that mor————————nin'. Oh

Pi-late's wife——, good Lord, she dreamt a dream—,

good Lord, 'bout an in-no-cent man——, good Lord, said who——

— want to seek— good Lord, old Pi—— late's work,

good Lord, come seek the man, a-huh—— good Lord, said

give me wa-ter, good Lord, I would wash— my hands—,

good Lord, I won't be guil——ty, good Lord, at an

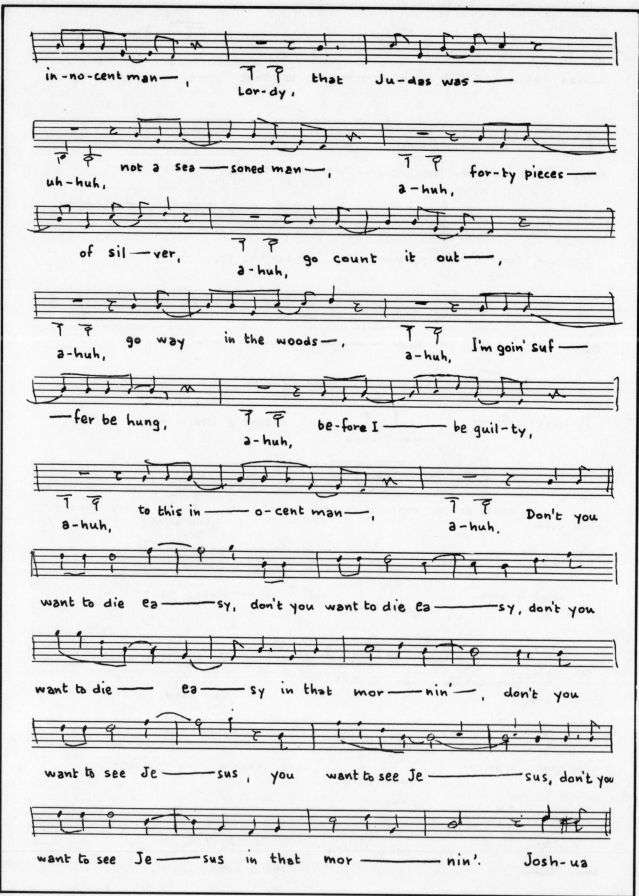

in-no-cent man——, Lor-dy, that Ju-das was——

uh-huh, not a sea——soned man——, a-huh, for-ty pieces——

of sil——ver, a-huh, go count it out——

a-huh, go way in the woods——, a-huh, I'm goin' suf——

——fer be hung, a-huh, be-fore I —— be guil-ty,

a-huh, to this in——o-cent man——, a-huh. Don't you

want to die ea——sy, don't you want to die ea——sy, don't you

want to die —— ea——sy in that mor——nin'——, don't you

want to see Je ——sus, you want to see Je ——sus, don't you

want to see Je ——sus in that mor —— nin'. Josh-ua

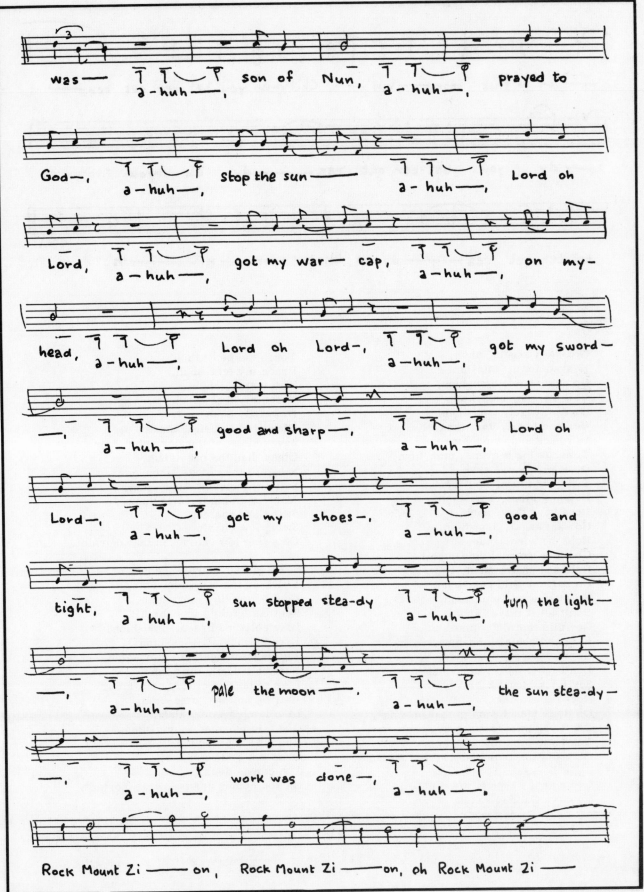

— on in that mor —— nin' ——. Chil-dren you bet-ter get rea ——

— dy,   you   bet-ter get rea —— dy, oh you

etc.

bet-ter get rea ——— dy in that mor — ni ——— n'.

Then:

God send angels, ahuh,
Heaven down, umn-hmn,
Go east angel, umn-hmn,
Veil the sun, umn-hmn,
Go east angel, umn-hmn,
Veil the moon, umn-hmn,
Sail back sun, umn-hmn,
Towards the heavens, umn,hmn,
Done your duty, ahuh,
Sail back moon, umn-hmn,
Drippin' blood, umn-hmn,
Done your duty, ahuh,
Go east angel, umn-hmn,
Hold the wind, ahuh,
God this mornin' umn-hmn,
Rule and chain, ahuh,
Go north angel, umn-hmn,
Hold the wind, umn-hmn,
Don't let it move, ahuh,
God this mornin', umn-hmn,
Rule and chain, umn-hmn,
Go west angel, umn-hmn,
Don't let it move, umn-hmn,
Say Rock Mount Zion,
Rock Mount Zion,
Oh Rock Mount Zion in that mornin',
Don't you want to die easy,
Don't you want to die easy,
Oh you want to die easy in that mornin'.

God's sent Gabriel, umn-hmn,
Go down Gabriel, ahuh,

Touch the sea, ahuh,
Brace my feet, ahuh,
Water side, ahuh,
Brace my feet, ahuh,
Dry land, ahuh,
Blow loud Gabriel, ahuh,
Seven claps of thunder, umn-hmn,
Other than the one, ahuh,
Spoke to the clouds, umn-hmn,
Sail away clouds, umn-hmn,
Make up in chair, umn-hmn,
Swing low chariot,
Swing low chariot,
Oh swing low chariot in that mornin'.

See God that mornin', ahuh,
Filled up the air, umn-hmn,
Feet be movin', umn-hmn,
Feet be shinin', umn-hmn,
Like polished brass, umn-hmn,
Eyes be movin', umn-hmn,
Zig-zags of lightnin', umn-hmn,
Hair be rollin', umn-hmn,
Like pillars of cloud, umn-hmn,
Hair be shinin', umn-hmn,
Like lamb's wool, ahuh,
God this mornin', umn-hmn,
Rule and chain, umn-hmn,
Over yon comes Jesus,
Yon comes Jesus,
Oh yon comes Jesus in that mornin'.

8. PRAYER

9. THE SUN WILL NEVER GO DOWN

Then:

Don't you feel like shouting sometimes,
    sometimes,
Don't you feel like shouting sometimes,
    sometimes,
The flowers are blooming forevermore.
Then the sun will never go down.

Don't you miss your mother sometimes,
    sometimes,
Don't you miss your mother sometimes,
    sometimes,
The flowers are blooming forevermore,
Then the sun will never go down.

10. THIS MAY BE YOUR LAST TIME

This may be your last time, this may be your last time, this may be your last time, may be your last time, I don't know (sis-ter).

Talk a-bout me much as you please, more you talk I'll bend my knees, may be your last time, I don't know (sis-ter), This may be your last time, this may be your last time, this may be your last time, may be your last time, I don't know. Way down yon-der by Jor-dan stream, Hear God's chil-dren tryin' to be re-deemed, may be your last time, I don't know, Meet Mis-ter Hy-po-crite on the street—,

first thing he show you his tongue in his cheek, may be your last time,

11. KING DAVID

King Da-vid was- (good Lord ——

—) a shep-herd boy— (good Lord ——) did-n't he kill Go—

-li-ath (good Lord —) and he shout for joy ——— (good Lord ——

—) Well the tall-est tree (good Lord —) in par-a-dise—

——— (good Lord —) them Christ-ians called it (good Lord ——

—) their tree of life —— (good Lord ——). Lit-tle Da-vid

play on your harp, hal-le ——lu —— (hal-le —— lu—), lit-tle Da-vid

play on —— your harp, hal-le —— lu, did-n't you prom-ise to

play on —— your harp, hal-le —— lu ——, hel-le-

-lu ——, did-n't you prom-ise to play on your harp, hal-le-

-lu. Just watch the sun —— (good Lord —) how stea-dy she

run (good Lord —) don't mind she catch you (good Lord ——) with your work un-

done (good Lord —). Little Da-vid play on your harp, hal-le-

-lu —— (hal-le-lu ——), little Da-vid play on —— your harp ——

——, (hal-le-lu ——), did-n't you prom-ise to play on your

harp, hal-le —— lu —— (hal-le —— lu), did-n't you prom-ise to

etc.

play on your harp hal-le-lu

Then:

You got a true way to find
Good Lord,
Mister hypocrite out.
Good Lord,
At the first thing gwine
Good Lord,
To the church and shout
Good Lord.
You goin' to meet Mr. Hyprocrite
Good Lord,
Comin' along the street,
Good Lord,
First thing he show you
Good Lord,
His tongue in his teeth.
Good Lord.

Little David play on hour harp...etc.

Just as soon as you cease
Good Lord,
Children, from your sins,
Good Lord,
This-a train will start
Good Lord,
It'll take you in.
Good Lord,
Well way down yonder
Good Lord,
By Jordan Stream
Good Lord,
You can hear God's children
Good Lord,
Tryin' to be redeemed.
Good Lord,
Ain't Jordan wide,
Good Lord,
Old Jordan wide,
Good Lord,
Well none don't cross,
Good Lord,
But the sanctified,
Good Lord.

Little David, play....etc.

Sister Mary goin' to heaven,
Good Lord,
On the springs (?) of the sun.
Good Lord,
When Mary got to heaven,
Good Lord,
...................was done.
Good Lord,
Just talk about me,
Good Lord,
Just as much as you please,
Good Lord,
But the more you talks
Good Lord,
I'm goin' to bend my knees.
Good Lord.

Little David, play....etc.

Ever since my soul
Good Lord,
Children, been set free,
Good Lord,
Satan act and lie, ...,
Good Lord,
At the root of the tree.
Good Lord,
Ain't Satan just like
Good Lord,
A snake in the grass,
Good Lord,
He's always walkin',
Good Lord,
In a Christian's path.
Good Lord,
Old Satan got on
Good Lord,
Them iron shoes.
Good Lord,
It's you better mind,
Good Lord,
Don't he step 'em on you.
Good Lord,

Little David, play....etc.

12. IT'S GETTING LATE IN THE EVENING

Lord it's get-tin' late over in the eve — nin' —,

Lord it's get-tin' late over in the eve — nin' —,

Children it's get-tin' late over in the eve — nin' —,

Lord it's get-tin' late over in the eve — nin' —, the

sun most down —. Don't you seal up your book, John —

—, Don't you seal up your book, John —,

Don't seal up- your book, John —

Don't you seal up your book, John —,

till you can sign my name —.

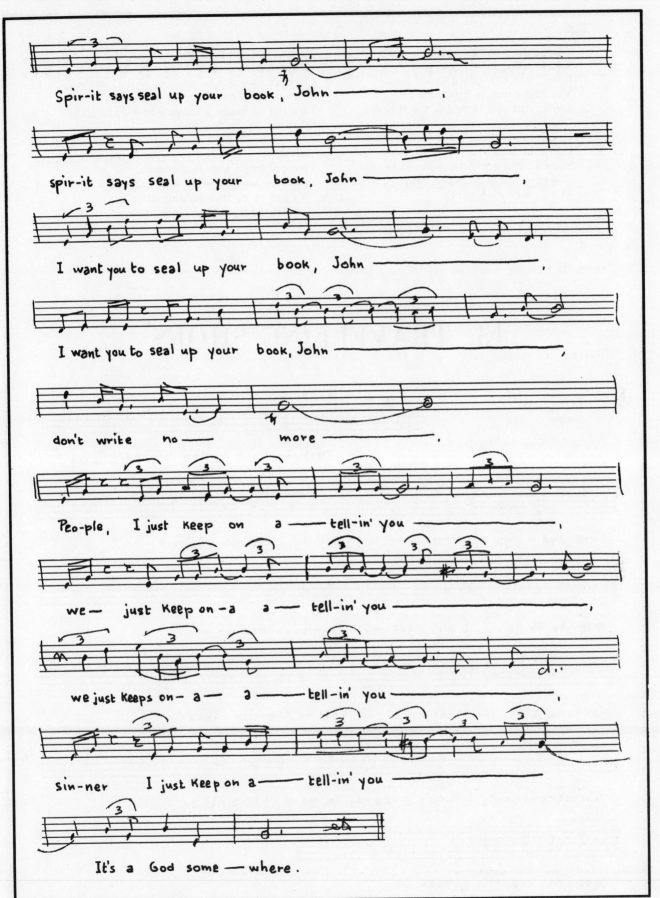

Spir-it says seal up your book, John _____.

spir-it says seal up your book, John _____,

I want you to seal up your book, John _____,

I want you to seal up your book, John _____,

don't write no __ more _____.

Peo-ple, I just keep on a __ tell-in' you _____,

we __ just keep on -a a __ tell-in' you _____,

we just keeps on- a __ a __ tell-in' you _____,

sin-ner I just keep on a __ tell-in' you _____

It's a God some __ where.

Then:

Children, you can come in my home,
You can come in my home,
Lord, you can come to my home,
You can come to my home,
Lord, and you'll find-a me there.

I'm goin' away to leave you,
I'm goin' away to leave you,
Sinner, I'm goin' away to leave you,
I'm goin' away to leave you,
And I can't stay here.

Lord, we got to make a move,
Have mercy Jesus, (....),
People, we got to make a move, move,
People, we got to make a move,
We got to make a move some day,
And we can't stay here.

Lord, we got to go to judgement,
We got to go into judgement,
People, we got to go into judgement,
We got to go into judgement,
Sister, and we can't tell when.

13. TRAVELLING SHOES

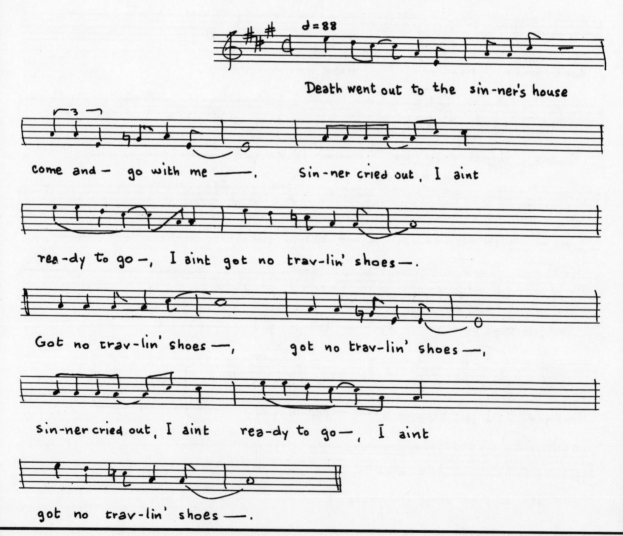

14. WONDER WHERE IS MY BROTHER GONE

Won-der where ——— is my— bro-ther gone ———? Won-der where ——— is my— bro-ther John ———? He is gone to the wil-der-ness, aint com-in' no more ———. Won-der where ——— will I— lie down ———? Won-der where ——— will I lie down ———? In some lone-some place Lord down on the ground ———. Won-der where ——— will I lie down ———? In some lone-some place Lord down on the ground ———.

15. DEATH IS AWFUL

Then:

Oh death is awful,
Oh death is awful,
Oh death is awful,
Spare me over another year.

If I was a flower in my bloom,
Make that cut me down so soon,
Oh death is awful,
Mmm death is awful,
Mmm death is awful,
Spare me over another year

Oh what is this that I can't see,
Well call that the angel over me,
Oh death is awful,
Ahh death is awful,
Oh death is awful,
Spare me over another year.

This is the way that death begins,
You stretch your limbs and close your eyes,
Oh death is awful,
Mmm death is awful,
Mmm death, just spare me over another year.

16. TROUBLED, LORD, I'M TROUBLED

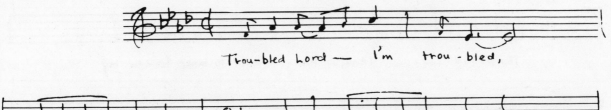

Trou-bled Lord — I'm trou-bled,

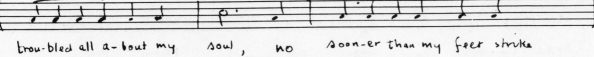

trou-bled all a-bout my soul, no soon-er than my feet strike

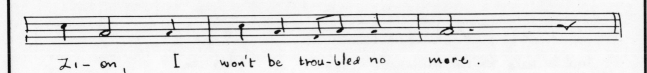

Zi-on, I won't be trou-bled no more.

Then:

Troubled, Lord, I'm troubled,
I'm troubled all about my soul,
No sooner than my feet strike Zion
I won't be troubled no more.

I'm wondering, Lord, I'm wondering,
I'm wondering about my soul,
Oh Lord
No sooner than my feet strike Zion
I won't be wondering any more.

I wonder where my mother,
I wonder where she's gone,
She's somewhere sitting in the kingdom
And she won't be troubled no more.

I'm grieving, Lord, I'm grieving,
I'm grieving about my soul,
No sooner than my feet strike Zion
I won't be grieving any more.

17. TRAMPING, TRAMPING

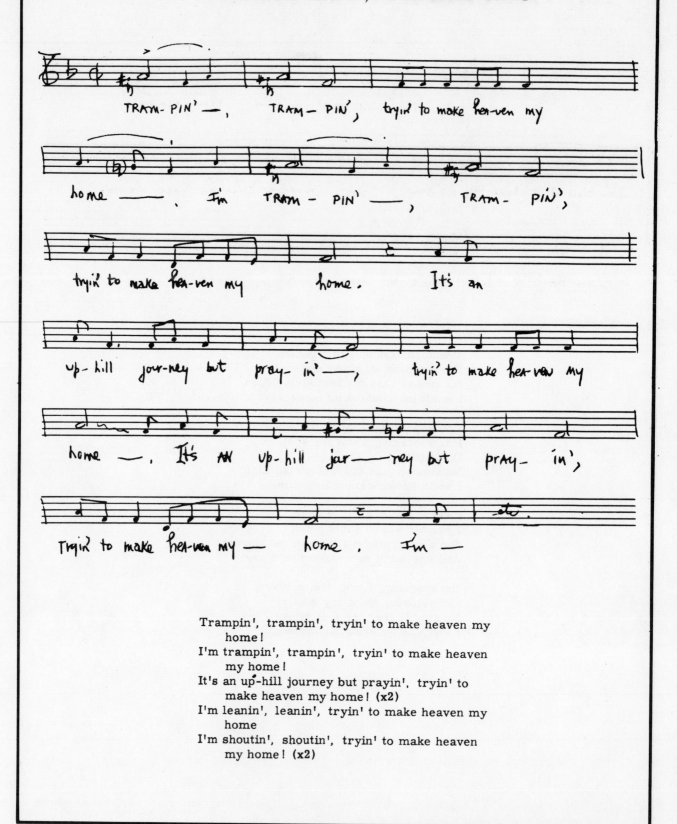

Trampin', trampin', tryin' to make heaven my
    home!
I'm trampin', trampin', tryin' to make heaven
    my home!
It's an up-hill journey but prayin', tryin' to
    make heaven my home! (x2)
I'm leanin', leanin', tryin' to make heaven my
    home
I'm shoutin', shoutin', tryin' to make heaven
    my home! (x2)

18. DEAR AND GONE

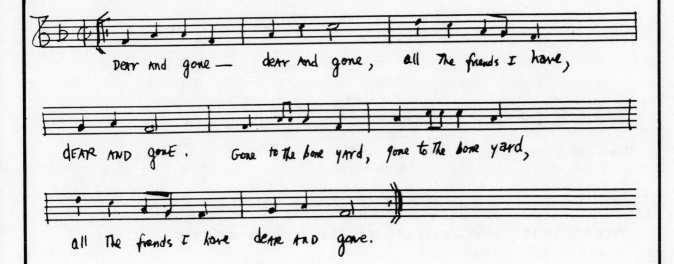

Dear and gone — dear and gone, all the friends I have,

DEAR AND GONE. Gone to the bone yard, gone to the bone yard,

all the friends I have dear and gone.

Then:

> Dear and gone, Lord! (x2)
> All the friends I have,
> Dear and gone!
>
> Gone to the bone yard! (x2)
> All the friends I have,
> Dear and gone!
>
> My poor mother! (x3)
> Dear and gone!
>
> Gone to the bone yard! (x3)
> Oh my Lord!
>
> Never turn back! (x3)
> Oh my Lord!
>
> My poor father! (x3)
> Dear and gone!
>
> Gone to the bone yard! (x3)
> Oh my Lord!

19. FREE AT LAST

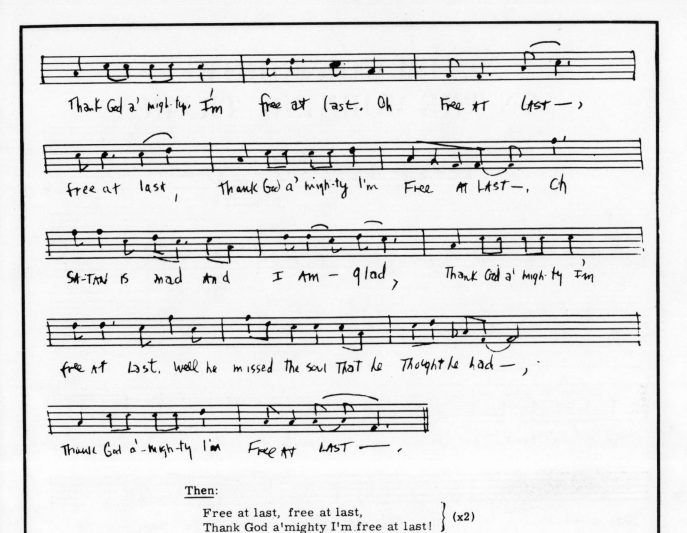

Thank God a'might-ty, I'm free at last. Oh Free at Last—,

free at last, thank God a'migh-ty I'm Free At Last—, Oh

SA-TAN is mad And I Am — glad, Thank God a'might-ty I'm

free at last. Well he missed the soul That he Thought he had—,

Thank God a'might-ty I'm Free At Last—.

Then:

> Free at last, free at last,
> Thank God a'mighty I'm free at last! ⎱ (x2)
> One day, one day, I was walkin' along,
> Thank God a'mighty I'm free at last!
> I met old Satan on my way,
> Thank God a'mighty I'm free at last!
> What you reckon old Satan said to me?
> Thank God a'mighty I'm free at last!
> Young man, young man, you're too young to
>   pray,
> Thank God a'mighty I'm free at last!
> If I'm too young to pray I ain't too young to
>   die,
> Thank God a'mighty I'm free at last!
> Oh free at last, free at last,
> Thank God a'mighty I'm free at last!
> Old Satan mad and I am glad,
> Thank God a'mighty I'm free at last!
> Well he missed his soul that he thought he had,
> Thank God a'mighty I'm free at last!

20. I'M GOING HOME ON THE MORNING TRAIN

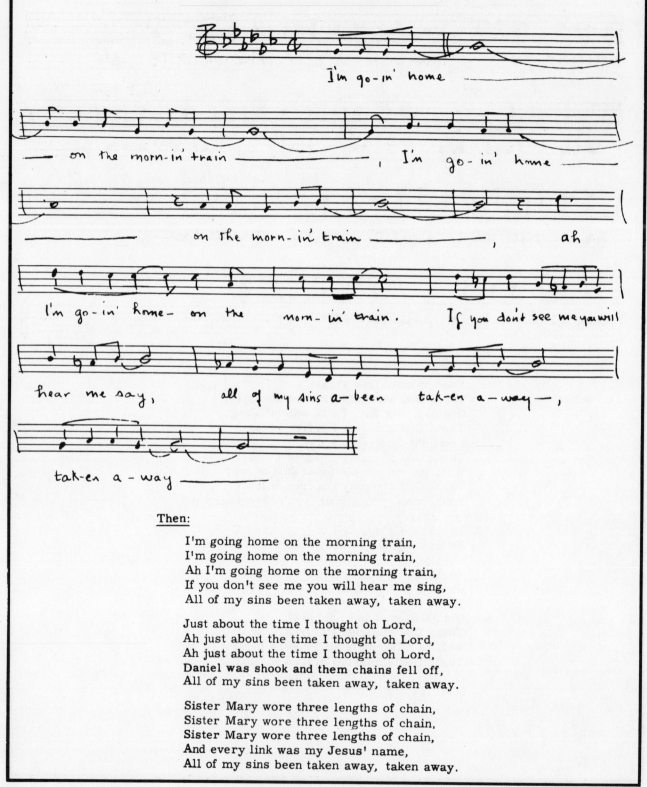

Then:

I'm going home on the morning train,
I'm going home on the morning train,
Ah I'm going home on the morning train,
If you don't see me you will hear me sing,
All of my sins been taken away, taken away.

Just about the time I thought oh Lord,
Ah just about the time I thought oh Lord,
Ah just about the time I thought oh Lord,
Daniel was shook and them chains fell off,
All of my sins been taken away, taken away.

Sister Mary wore three lengths of chain,
Sister Mary wore three lengths of chain,
Sister Mary wore three lengths of chain,
And every link was my Jesus' name,
All of my sins been taken away, taken away.

21. JESUS GOING TO MAKE UP MY DYING BED

oh — dont' you wor-ry 'bout me dy – in'! Oh — don't you wor-ry 'bout me dy – in'! Oh — don't you wor-ry 'bout me dy – in'! Je-sus goin' to make up my dy – in' bed —!

Then:

> Oh, don't you worry 'bout me dyin'!
> Oh, don't worry 'bout me dyin'!
> Oh, worry 'bout me dyin'!
> Jesus goin' to make up muh dyin' bed!
> Oh, I been in this valley!
> Oh, I been in this valley!
> Oh, I been in this valley!
> Jesus goin' to make up muh dyin' bed!
> Ah, when you see me dyin'
> I don't want you to cry.
> All I want you do for me
> Just low my dyin' head.
> Ah I'm sleepin' on Jesus!
> Ah, sleepin' on Jesus!
> Oh, I'm sleepin' on Jesus!
> Jesus goin' to make up my dyin' bed!

22. OH DEATH HAVE MERCY

"Once was a man weakened. Death come in his room. Well, he has been promising and promising he was going to pray. But he had put it off too late. And there was come one young man, he did, and help his partner serve God. And he wouldn't serve God, and Death gave him time to talk to him. I believe I'll sing about that man, a few verses."

Oh Death —, have mer —cy, oh —,

oh Death, have mer —cy, oh —, oh— Death, just

spare me o-(ver a —noth-er year).* Oh — Death, have (mer-

—cy), 5h, oh — (Death, have mer — cy),

oh — Death —, just spare me o—(ver a—noth-er year)

Here man said, Death don't cut me down so soon, a right young flower just

in my bloom, Lord. Oh — (Death—), have mer —cy,

— oh —— (Death—), get rea——dy, oh ——

* Words in parentheses sung only by second voice.

Death, just spare me o—(ver a —noth-er year).

Here man said, hur-ry Spir—it, hur-ry down soon,

Death's here walk-in' all   through my room, Lord.   Oh ——

Death, have mer-cy,   oh —— Death, get rea-dy,

oh —— Death— just spare me o—(ver a—noth-er year).

Here Death say,   man oh man, my   name is Death,   I

stink— like sin-, o-pen the   door of your heart—, let

Death walk in, Lord.   Oh —— Death, have mer-cy,

oh —— Death, have mer——cy,   oh — Death—, just

spare me o——ver a —noth-er year.   Here man said,

23. COME ON UP TO BRIGHT GLORY

Then:

You don't hear me prayin' here,
You can't find me nowhere, children,
Come on up to bright glory,
I'll be waitin' up there.
I'll be waitin' up there my Lord,
I'll be waitin' up there,
Come on up to bright glory,
I'll be waitin' up there.

You can't hear me when I pray down here, Etc.

You can't hear me preach down here, Etc.

You can't hear me when I shout down here, Etc.

24. I'M CLIMBING UP THE HILLS OF MT. ZION

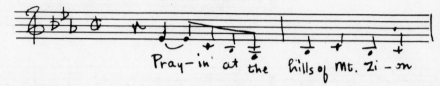

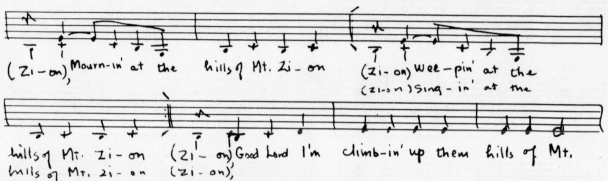

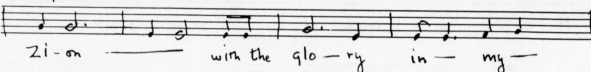

Then:

Praying at the hills of Mt. Zion,
Mourning at the hills of Mt. Zion,
Weeping at the hills of Mt. Zion,
Singing at the hills of Mt. Zion,
Good Lord I'm climbing up them hills of
    Mt. Zion
Oh Lord with the glory in my soul.

Preaching at the hills of Mt. Zion,
Crying at the hills of Mt. Zion,
Toiling at the hills of Mt. Zion,
Good Lord I'm climbing up them hills of
    Mt. Zion
Oh Lord with the glory in my soul.

Shouting at the hills of Mt. Zion,
Groaning at the hills of Mt. Zion,
Climbing at the hills of Mt. Zion,
Oh Lord I'm climbing up them hills of
    Mt. Zion
With the glory in my soul.

25. PLUMB THE LINE

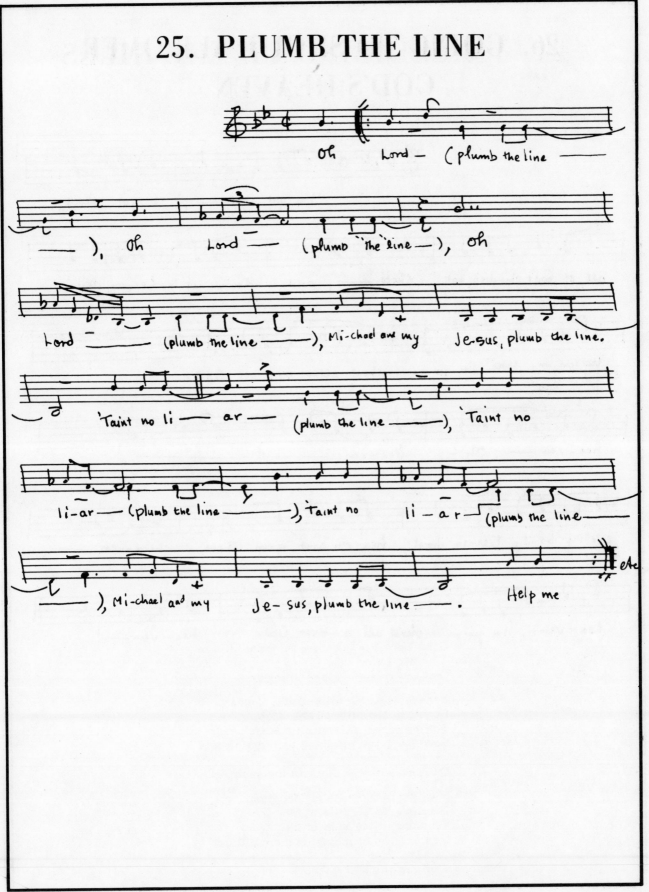

26. GOING TO SHOUT ALL OVER GOD'S HEAVEN

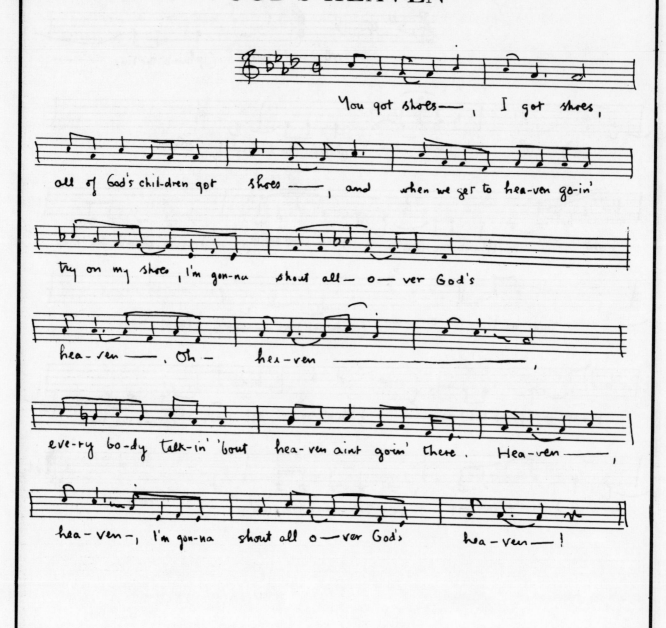

27. LORD. I'M WAITING ON YOU

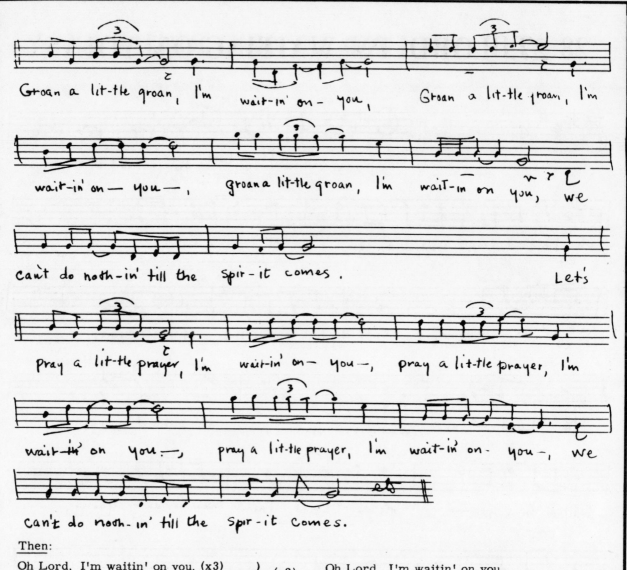

Groan a lit-tle groan, I'm wait-in' on - you, Groan a lit-tle groan, I'm wait-in' on - you —, groan a lit-tle groan, I'm wait-in on you, we can't do noth-in' till the spir-it comes. Let's

Pray a lit-tle prayer, I'm wait-in' on - you —, pray a lit-tle prayer, I'm wait-in on you —, pray a lit-tle prayer, I'm wait-in on - you —, we

can't do noth-in' till the spir-it comes.

Then:

Oh Lord, I'm waitin' on you, (x3)
Can't do nothin' till the spirit comes. } (x2)

Down here Lord, I'm waitin' on you, (x3)
Can't do nothin' till the spirit comes.

Groan a little groan I'm waitin' on you, (x3)
Well I can't do nothin' till the spirit comes.

Let's pray a little prayer, I'm waitin' on you,
Pray a little prayer, I'm waitin' on you,
Pray a little prayer, I'm waitin' on you,
We can't do nothin' till the spirit comes.

Oh Lord, I'm waitin' on you, (x3)
We can't do nothin' till the spirit comes.

Down here cryin', I'm waitin' on you, (x3)
Well I can't do nothin' till the spirit comes.

Groan a groan, I'm waitin' on you, (x3)
Well I can't do nothin' till the spirit comes.

Oh Lord, I'm waitin' on you,
Oh Lord, we're waitin' on you,
Oh Lord, waitin' on you,
Well I can't do nothin' till the spirit comes.

Down here Lord, oh waitin' on you,
Down here Lord, it's waitin' on you,
Down here Lord, it's waitin' on you,
Well I can't do nothin' till the spirit comes.

Later:

Just preach a little sermon, oh waitin' on you,
Preach a little sermon whilst waitin' on you,
Preach a little sermon, I'm waitin' on you,
Well I can't do nothin' till the spirit comes

Shout a little shout, oh waitin' on you(x3)
Well I can't do nothin' till the spirit comes.

Etc.

28. TIP AROUND MY BED RIGHT EASY

Jes' tip a-round my bed right ea — sy, right
ea — sy, right ea-sy —, jes' tip a-round my bed right
ea — sy, and bring God's ser—vant — home. Jes'

Then:

> Jes' tip around muh bed right easy,
> Right easy, right easy,
> Jes' tip around muh bed right easy,
> And bring God's servant home!

> Jes' low down the chariot right easy,
> Right easy, right easy,
> Jes' low down the chariot right easy,
> And bring God's servant home!

> Jes' turn muh bed around right easy,
> Right easy, right easy,
> Jes' turn muh bed around right easy,
> And bring God's servant home!

> Jes' turn muh pillow 'round right easy,
> Right easy, right easy,
> Jes' turn muh pillow 'round right easy,
> And bring God's servant home!

> Jes' turn muh cover back right easy,
> Right easy, right easy,
> Jes' turn muh cover back right easy,
> And bring God's servant home!

> Oh low down, death, right easy,
> Right easy, right easy,
> Jes' low down, death, right easy,
> And bring God's servant home!

29. LOOK HOW THEY DONE MY LORD

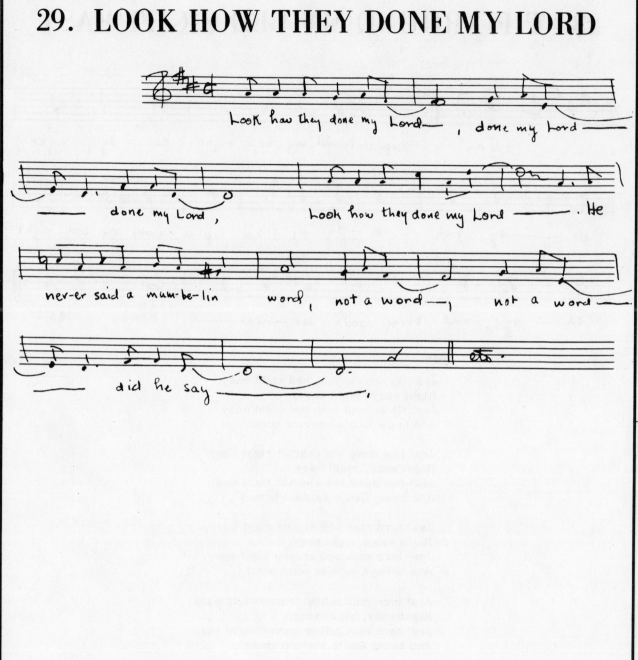

30. MY GOD AINT NO LYING MAN

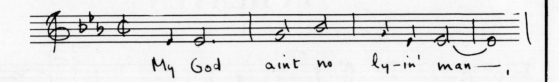

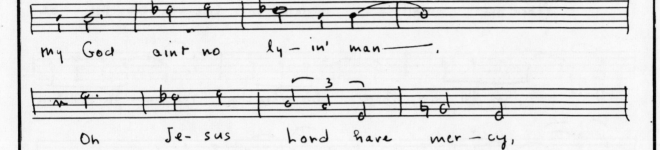

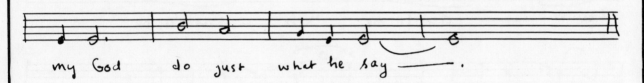

My God aint no ly-in' man —,
my God aint no ly — in' man —.
Oh Je-sus Lord have mer —cy,
my God do just what he say —.

Then:

My God ain't no lying man,
Oh my God ain't no lying man,
Oh Jesus, Lord have mercy,
My God do just what he say.

My God promised me a home,
Oh my God promised me a home,
Oh Jesus, Lord have mercy,
My God promised me a home.

I got a home where the gambler can't go,
I got a home where the gambler can't go,
Oh Jesus, Lord have mercy.
I got a home where the gambler can't go.

My God do just what he say,
Oh my God do just what he say,
Oh Jesus, Lord have mercy,
My God do just what he say.

You lie sick and raise the dead,
Ah you lie sick and raise the dead,
Oh Jesus, Lord have mercy,
You lie sick and raise the dead.

31. WHEN THE ROLL IS CALLED IN HEAVEN

32. I'M STANDING IN A SAFETY ZONE

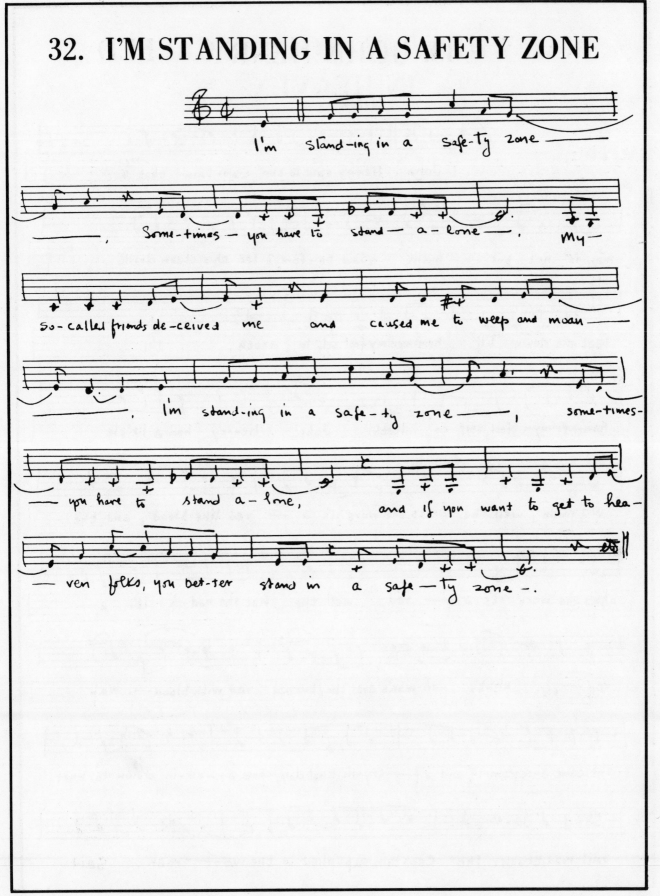

I'm stand-ing in a safe-ty zone —, Some-times — you have to stand — a-lone —, My — so-called friends de-ceived me and caused me to weep and moan —, I'm stand-ing in a safe-ty zone —, some-times — you have to stand a-lone, and if you want to get to hea-ven folks, you bet-ter stand in a safe-ty zone —.

33. JOHN HENRY

tell me wom-an what's troublin' your mind. Says I'm go-in' where my man fell

dead, says I'm go-in' where my man fell dead, says I'm

go-in' where my man fell dead, says I'm go-in' where my man fell

dead. He done ham-mered to death—, he done his fool self

ham-mered his fool self to death. John Hen-ry had a-noth-er

wom-an, well her name was Pearl-y Anne. Well

Pearl-y Anne she heard a-bout this man's death, well what you reck-on she

said? Said be-fore I stand to see my man go down, says

give me a ten pound ham-mer, goin' to hook it on to the

right of my arm, goin' to bring me a nine pound ham-mer, goin' to

looked in his moth-er's face—. Well his moth-er looked down at her

ba-by's face—, said tell me son what you worryin' a-bout? The

last lov-in' words she ever heard that boy say—, mamma I want to make a rail-road

man, mamma I want to make a rail-road man. I'm goin' to

die like pa-pa died——, I'm goin' to die like pa-pa—

died. Son—, pa-pa was a steel driv-in' man, son,

pa-pa was a steel driv-in' man. But he ham-mered his fool self to

death, but he ham-mered his fool self to death. John

Hen-ry had a-no-ther lit-tle ba-by boy—, he was ly-in' in the and
cra-dle kick-in'

cry-in', ev-ery time mam-ma rocked the cra-dle bump-ty-bump-a-lump, I

want to make a rail-road man, say I   want to make a rail-road

man. Goin' to   die   like   pa-pa   died,   I want to die like pa-pa—

died. Son your dad-dy was a steel driv-in' man,   Your dad-dy was a steel driv-in'

man.   But he   ham-mered his fool self to   death—,   but he   ham-mered his fool self to

death.   When   Hen-ry was tween them   moun-tains the   Cap-tain saw him go-in'

down——.   He sup-plied to Hen-ry one   day, tried to pac-i-fy—   his

mind—,   says Hen-ry you know you's a   nat-u-ral man.   Well

what you reck-on that he   said—?   Says the steam drill drive—   one

ham-mer by steam, says the steam drill drive one—   ham-mer by air—.   Now

how in the world you 'spect to   beat steam down?   He says how in the world you 'spect to

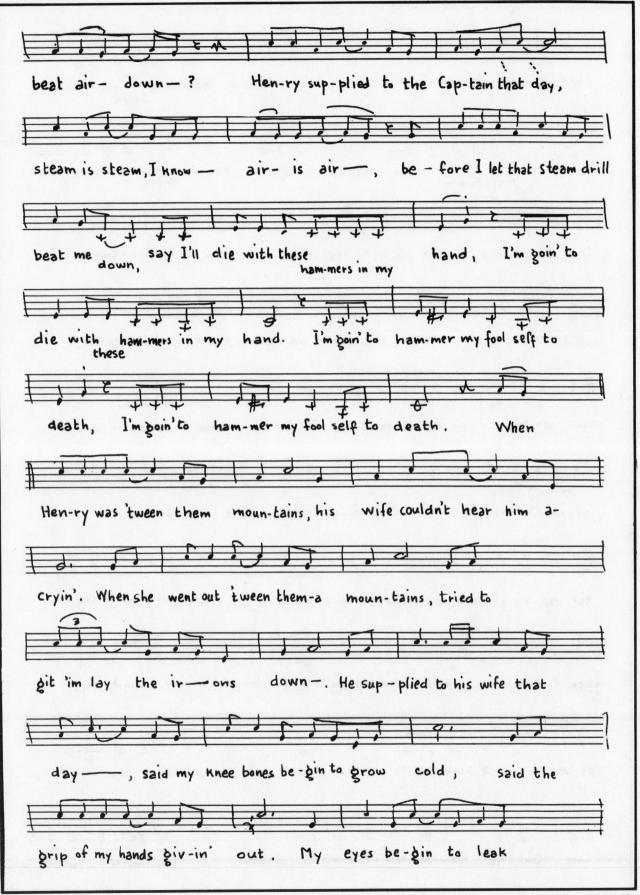

wa-ter —. Be —fore I — lay- these ham-mers down I'll

die — with these ham-mers in my hand, I'm goin' to die with these ham-mers in my hand.

Take John Hen-ry to the cem-e-ter-y, lay him in his lone-some

gra — ve —, while she walked up there to the foot of the grave,

cast her eyes — in her hus-band's face —, come a-scream-in' and a-

cry-in' that day, Preach-er looked 'round in the wom-an's face —,

tell me wom-an what you scream-in' a-bout —? Last lov-in' words she sup-

plied to him , taint but one thing that's a —trou-bl-in' my mind, that

cer-tain-ly was a true man to me, that cer-tain-ly was a true man to

me. But he ham-mered his fool self to death, he ham-mered his fool self to

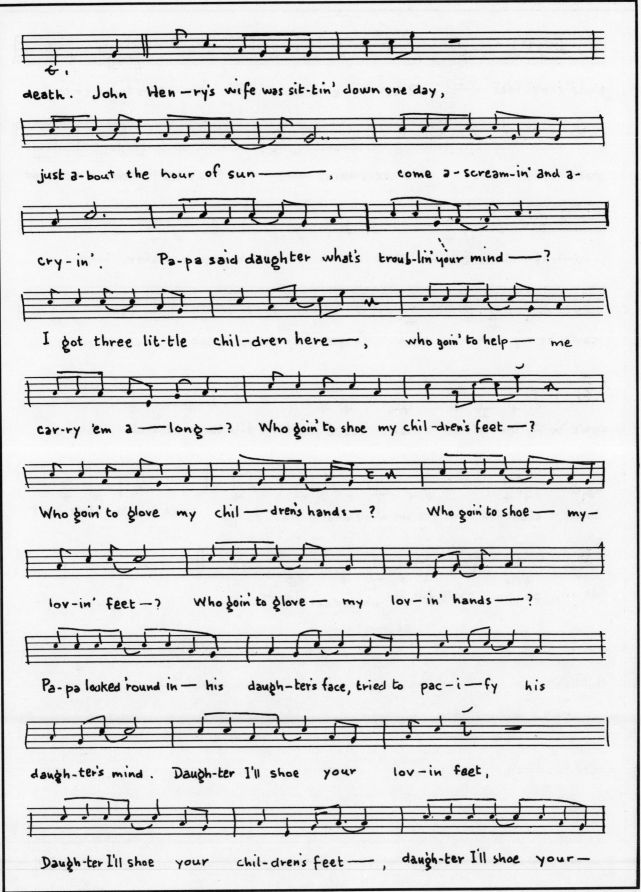

death. John Hen—ry's wife was sit-tin' down one day,

just a-bout the hour of sun———, come a-scream-in' and a-

cry-in'. Pa-pa said daughter what's troub-lin'your mind———?

I got three lit-tle chil-dren here———, who goin' to help— me

car-ry 'em a—long—? Who goin' to shoe my chil-dren's feet —?

Who goin' to glove my chil—dren's hands— ? Who goin to shoe— my—

lov-in' feet—? Who goin to glove— my lov-in' hands———?

Pa-pa looked 'round in— his daugh-ter's face, tried to pac-i—fy his

daugh-ter's mind. Daugh-ter I'll shoe your lov-in feet,

Daugh-ter I'll shoe your chil-dren's feet——, daugh-ter I'll shoe your—

child-ren's feet——. Broth-er he looked— in his sis—ter's face, tried to

pac-i-fy his sis-ter's mind———, sis-ter I'll kiss— your

ro—sy—cheeks. But you can't be my lov-in' man, bro-ther

can't be my lov-in' man. Pa-pa can't be my lov-in' man, pa-pa

can't be my lov-in'—— man. 'Cause you can't file the whole deal—

down, bro-ther can't file the whole deal down. Pa-pa can't file the whole deal

down, pa-pa can't file the whole deal 'down.

34. BLACK WOMAN

Well I said come here Black Wo——man, Ah—

hmm! Ah- hmm, don't you

hear me cryin' oh— Lor- dy ——!

Ah- hmm, I say run here Black Wo-man—

I want you to sit on Black Dad-dy's—

Knee, Lord! Ah- hmm, I know your

house feel lone-some, oh don't you hear me whoop-in' oh—

Lor- dy ——! Don't your house feel lone-some when your

bis-cuit rol-ler gone, Lord help my cry-in' time don't your

house feel lone-some, Mam-ma when your bis-cuit rol-ler gone! I say my

house feel lone-some, I know you hear me cry-in' oh —

Ba - by ————! Ah — hmm, ah when I

looked in my kit-chen Mam-ma, and I went

all through my dinin' room! Ah —

hmm, when I woke up this mor-ni — —

—in' I found my bis-cuit rol-ler done

gone ————! I'm goin' to Tex-as Mam-ma, just to

hear the wild ox moan, Lord help my cry-in' time I'm goin' to Tex-as

Mam-ma do you hear the wild ox moan!

feel su – per –sti – tious Mam-ma,   'bout my hog–gin' bread

Lord help my hun-gry time, I feel su-per-sti-tious Ba-by 'bout my

hog-gin' bread! Ah — hmm,   Oh Babe I

feel su-per-sti-tious ——— ,   I say—

'sti-tious Black Wo-man——!   Ah —hmm,

ah   you hear me cry ——————— in'—,   a-bout I

done got hun-gry— oh —   Lor-dy ———!   Oh Mam-ma I

feel su-per-sti-tious ———————————————

a-bout my   hog-gin'   Lord God it's

my   bread ——————!

I want you tell me Mam-ma —— Ah —

hmm I hear me cry-in' oh — Mam-ma —! Ah —

hmm I want you tell me Black Wo-man,

oh where did you stay last night ——? I

love you Black Wo—man, I tell the whole wide world I do—, Lord

help your hap-py black time I love you Ba-by, and I tell the world I

do! Ah–hmm, I love you Black Wo-man—, I know you

hear me whoop-in' Black Ba-by! Ah–hmm, I

love you Black Wo-man —— and I'll

tell your Dad-dy on you, Lord—!

35. WATER ON THE WHEEL

Wa—ter boy, wa—ter boy!

Wa—ter boy, wa—ter boy! Wa—ter on the whee—l,

how does the sun shine that I feel,

lit—tle wa—ter time, hey ——, lit—tle wa——ter boy,

lit—tle wa——ter time, hey ——, lit—tle wa——ter boy.

Wa—ter on the whee ——l how does the

sun shine ——— that I feel, lit—tle wat——er

boy.

36. CAPTAIN HOLLER HURRY

The Cap-tain hol-ler hur—ry——, goin' to take my time——. Say the Cap-tain hol-ler hur—ry——, goin' to take my time——. Say he mak-in' mon-ey—— and I'm tryin' to make time—. Say he can lose his job—— but I can't lose mine——. I aint got long to tar—ry——, just stop by here——. I aint got long to tar—ry——, just stop by here——. Boys if you got—— long—— you bet-ter move a-long—

37. THE CAPTAIN CAN'T READ

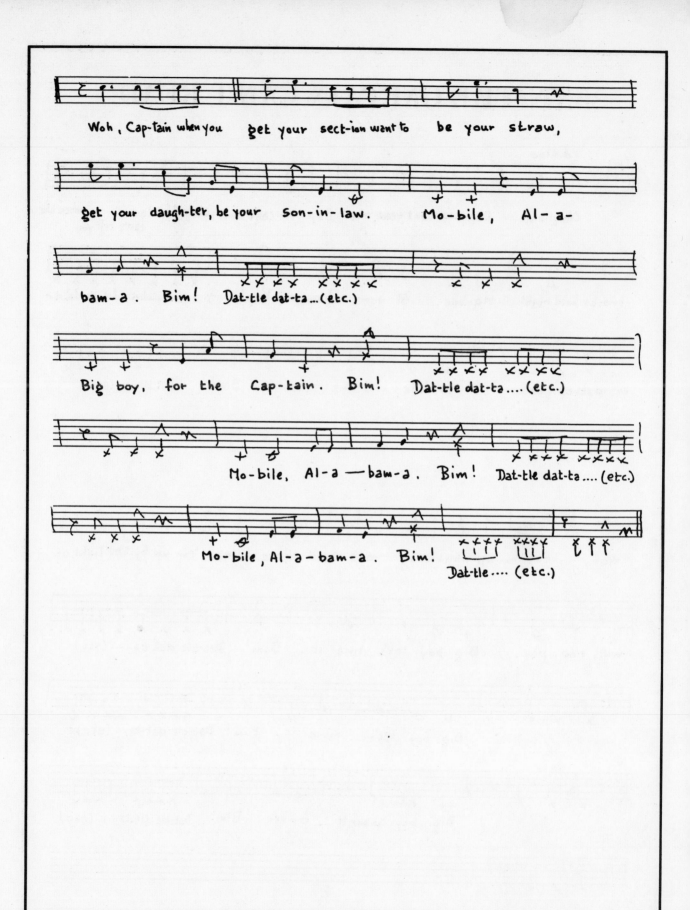

Woh, Cap-tain when you get your sect-ion want to be your straw,

get your daugh-ter, be your son-in-law. Mo-bile, Al-a-

bam-a. Bim! Dat-tle dat-ta ... (etc.)

Big boy, for the Cap-tain. Bim! Dat-tle dat-ta .... (etc.)

Mo-bile, Al-a —— bam-a. Bim! Dat-tle dat-ta .... (etc.)

Mo-bile, Al-a-bam-a. Bim! Dat-tle .... (etc.)

38. NOW YOUR MAN DONE GONE

♩=88

Now your man done gone, now your man done gone —, now your man done gone to the coun—ty farm —, now your man done gone ——. Ba—by

Then:

Baby please don't go, (3)
Back to Baltimore,
Baby please don't go.

Turn your lamp down low, (3)
And Baby please don't go,
Baby please don't go.

You know I loves you so, (3)
And Baby please don't go,
Baby please don't go.

I beg you all night long, (3)
And night before,
Baby please don't go.

Now your man done come, (3)
From the county farm,
Now your man done come.

Baby please don't go, (3)
Back to Baltimore,
Baby please gon't go.

I'm goin' to walk your log, (2)
And if you throw me off,
I'm goin' to walk your log.

39. SHE DONE GOT UGLY

Says huh Ju—lie—, hul-lo gal—. Says

huh Ju—lie—, hul-lo gal——. Says

ear-ly in the mor-nin' ba—by—, half past four. Says

ear-ly in the mor-nin' ba—by—, oh half past four. I

come to your win-dow baby, knocked on the door. Says get—

a-way from my win-dow ba-by—, quit knock-in' on my door. Says

got a-no-ther man ba-by, don't want you no more—. Says

huh gal ba-by—, done got ug-ly—. Says

huh Ju—lie——, you done got ug-ly—. Says

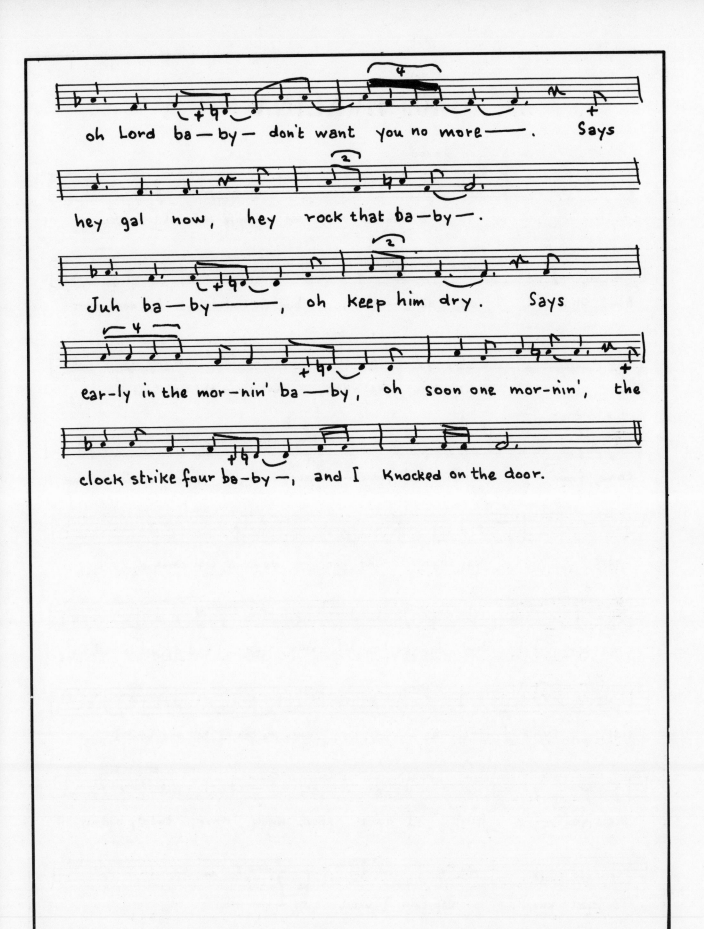

oh Lord ba—by— don't want you no more——. Says

hey gal now, hey rock that ba—by—.

Juh ba—by———, oh keep him dry. Says

ear—ly in the mor—nin' ba—by, oh soon one mor—nin', the

clock strike four ba—by—, and I knocked on the door.

40. EVALINA

♩ = 100

I want to — see my wife and chil-dren—.

Bim! Oh yes I do, do——, bud-dy bud-dy yes I do—

Cap-tain Wal-ker, where in the world did you

come from—? Bim! When'd you come here, here, bud-dy when'd you come

here? Cap-tain send me down a cool drink of

wa-ter—. Bim! Just to heal my side, side, bud-dy just to heal my

side. Ev-a—li-na——, when you gon-na tell me what I

asked you—? Bim! I don't know, know, know, bud-dy bud-dy

I don't know. Cap-tain I want to—

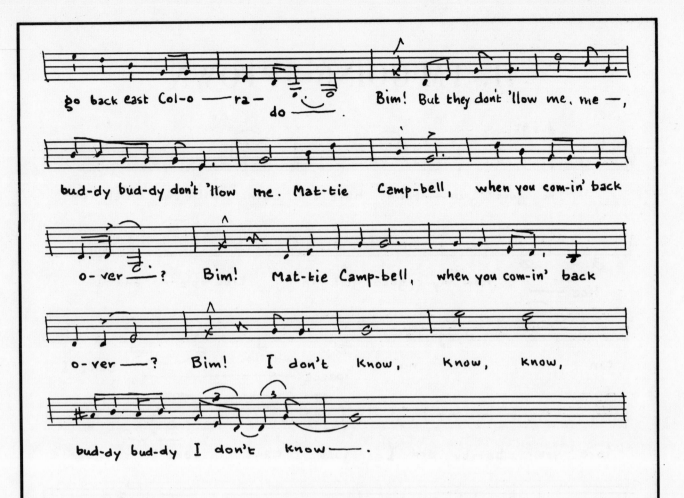

go back east Col-o ——— ra— do ——— . Bim! But they don't 'llow me, me —,

bud-dy bud-dy don't 'llow me. Mat-tie Camp-bell, when you com-in' back

o-ver ——? Bim! Mat-tie Camp-bell, when you com-in' back

o-ver —? Bim! I don't Know, know, know,

bud-dy bud-dy I don't know——.

41. I'M GOING UPTOWN

ri-ver and I looked it up and down ———, thought I'd

see my good girl when she walk—in' cross the

town —————————, I tell—— my

ba ———— by why—— she come back

home ———————, and I had—— no-

lov——in' babe since you been

gone ————————— etc

Then:

I tell my woman,
    tell her Lord for me,
Lord she can't quit me
    and it ain't no use of tryin'.
But my baby caught the train and I
    swore (.........)
Singin' to her that she can't quit me,
    Lord it ain't no use of tryin'.
Oh I tear uptown in the mornin' have a
    talk with the chief police,
'Cause Rena in trouble and I cannot
    see no peace.

42. HEY RUFUS

Hey Ru-fus, hey boy——, where in the world—— you
been so long? Hey bud-dy, hey boy——. Well
—— I been in the jun-gle ————, aint go-in' there no
more. Well I been in the jun————gle, aint go-in there no
more ——. Hey Ru-fus, hey—— boy.

43. WOH HOO

oo   woh hoo-oo   woh hoo ——
woh hoo-oo   woh hoo ——
yeh ee-ee   yeh hee ——
woh hoo-oo   woh hoo ——
yeh ee-ee   yeh hee ——

44. I'M GOING DOWN THE ROAD

45. FATHER'S FIELD CALL

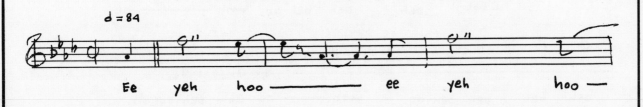

— hoo hoo — bay hoo — bay —

— Al — lay come on!

46. CHILDREN'S FIELD CALL

Yeh eh-beh-oo eh —— oo eh — oo

eh —— oo yeh beh-oo yeh — oo yeh beh beh

beh-oo woh —— oo woh oh yeh woh-oo woh — oo

yeh — beh-oo eh —— oo eh — oo eh — beh-oo —

beh beh beh beh-oo woh ——— oo

beh beh beh beh-oo woh —— oo eh — beh-oo oh

47. GIVE MY HEART EASE

48. LITTLE LAP DOG

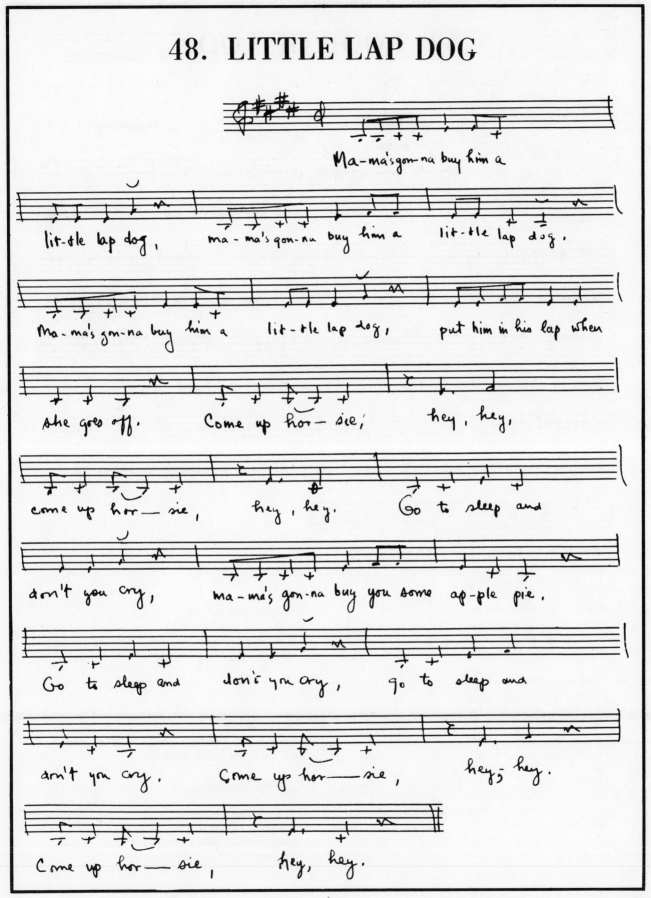

49. LOOP DE LOO

Then:

Here we go loop do loo,
Here we go loop de loo,
Here we go loop de loo,
All on a Saturday night.

I put my left hand in,
I take my left hand out,
I give my left hand a shake, shake, shake,
And turn my body about.

(CHORUS)

I put my right foot in,
I take my right foot out,
I give my right foot a shake, shake, shake,
And turn my body about.

(CHORUS)

I put my left foot in,
I take my left foot out,
I give my left foot a shake, shake, shake,
And turn my body about.

(CHORUS)

I put my big head in,
I take my big head out,
I give my big head a shake, shake, shake,
And turn my body about.

(CHORUS)

I put my big self in,
I take my big self out,
I give my big self a shake, shake, shake,
And turn my body about.

50. MARY MACK

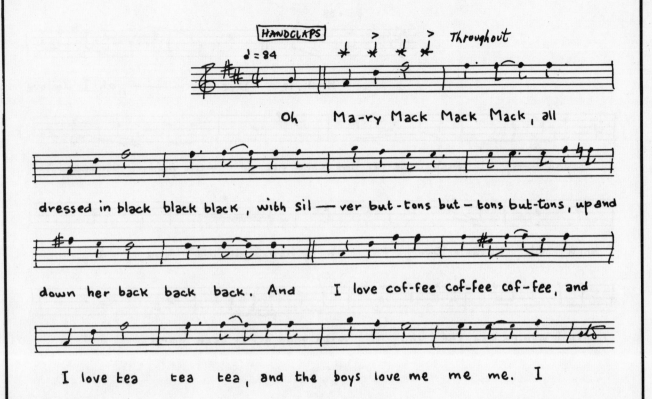

HANDCLAPS

♩ = 84

Throughout

Oh Ma-ry Mack Mack Mack, all

dressed in black black black, with sil — ver but-tons but-tons but-tons, up and

down her back back back. And I love cof-fee cof-fee cof-fee, and

I love tea tea tea, and the boys love me me me. I

Then:

I went to the river, river, river,
And I couldn't get across, 'cross, 'cross,
And I paid five dollars, dollars, dollars,
For the old grey horse, horse, horse.

And the horse wouldn't pull, pull, pull,
I swapped him for a bull, bull, bull,
And the bull wouldn't holler, holler, holler,
I swapped him for a dollar, dollar, dollar.

And the dollar wouldn't spend, spend, spend,
I put it in the grass, grass, grass,
And the grass wouldn't grow, grow, grow,
I got my hoe, hoe, hoe.

And the hoe wouldn't chop, chop, chop,
I took it to the shop, shop, shop,
And the shop made money, money, money,
Like the bees made homey, honey, honey.

See that yonder, yonder, yonder,
In the jay-bird town, town, town,
Where the women gotta work, work, work,
Till the sun goes down, down, down,

Well, I eat my meat, meat, meat,
And I gnaw my bone, bone, bone,
Well, good-bye honey, honey, honey,
I'm going on home.

51. KUSHIE DYE YO

Kush-ie Dye-yo ——, oh I do love you ——, I wish I ne-ver had seed you, I wish you'd ne-ver been born. Oh Kush-ie Dye Yo, oh how I do love you, I wish I nev-er had seed you, I wish you'd nev-er been born.

52. MAY GO ROUND THE NEEDLE

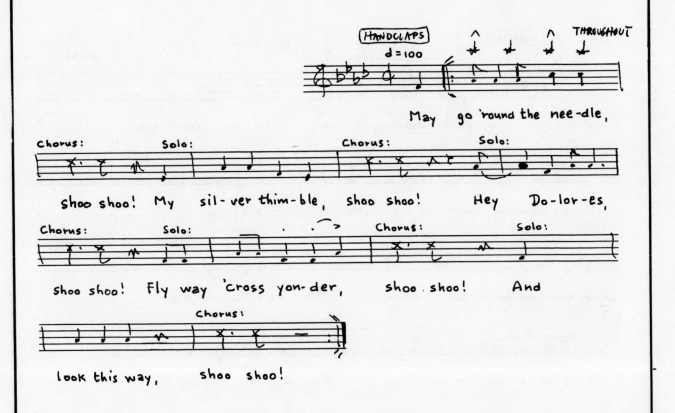

May go 'round the nee-dle,

Chorus: Solo: Chorus: Solo:

shoo shoo! My sil-ver thim-ble, shoo shoo! Hey Do-lor-es,

Chorus: Solo: Chorus: Solo:

shoo shoo! Fly way 'cross yon-der, shoo shoo! And

Chorus:

look this way, shoo shoo!

53. AMASEE

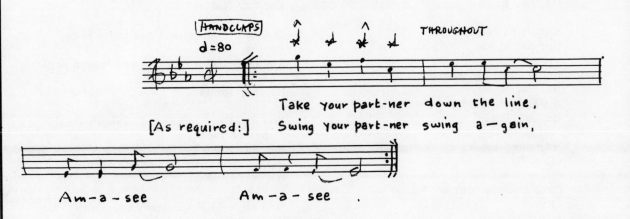

Take your part-ner down the line,

[As required:] Swing your part-ner swing a-gain,

Am-a-see   Am-a-see .

54. ROSIE DARLING ROSIE

Ro-sie dar-ling Ro-sie,   ha ha Ro—sie.

Ro-sie dar-ling Ro—sie,   ha ha Ro—sie.

Way down yon-der in Bal-ti-more,   ha ha Ro—sie,

need no car-pet on my floor,   ha ha Ro—sie.

Then:

Grab your partner and follow me,
Ha, ha, Rosie.
Let's go down by Galilee,
Ha, ha, Rosie.

Rosie, darling, Rosie.
Ha, ha, Rosie.

Rosie, darling, hurry,
Ha, ha, Rosie.
If you don't mind you gonna get left.
Ha, ha, Rosie.

Way down yonder by Baltimore.
(Etc.)

Grab your partner an' follow me,
(Etc.)

Rosie, darling, Rosie,
Ha, ha, Rosie.
Rosie, darling hurry.
Ha, ha, Rosie.

Some folks say preachers won't steal,
Ha, ha, Rosie.
But I caught two in my cornfield,
Ha, ha, Rosie.

One had a bushel and one had a peck,
Ha, ha, Rosie.
The baby had a roasting ear 'round her
neck,
Ha, ha, Rosie.

You steal my partner, you won't steal
her no more,
Ha, ha, Rosie.
Better stay from 'round my door.
Ha, ha, Rosie.

Stop right still and study yourself,
Ha, ha, Rosie.
See that fool where she got left,
Ha, ha, Rosie.

55. GREEN GREEN ROCKY ROAD

Green, green, rock-y road, some la-dy's green rock-y road. Tell me who you love, rock-y road, tell me who you love, rock—y road.

Min-nie Town. Dear Miss Min-nie your name's been called, come take a seat be—side the wall, give her a kiss and let her go—, she'll ne-ver sit in that chair no more.

56. JUST WATCH THAT LADY

I been all a-round my
last time, last time, last time, I been all a-round my
last time, young la-dy hold the key. Just watch that la-dy how she hold the
key, just watch that la-dy how she hold the key, young
la-dy hold the key. I

57. SANGAREE

Get on board, San-ga-ree, says
get on the road, San-ga-ree, we're a sor-ry team—,

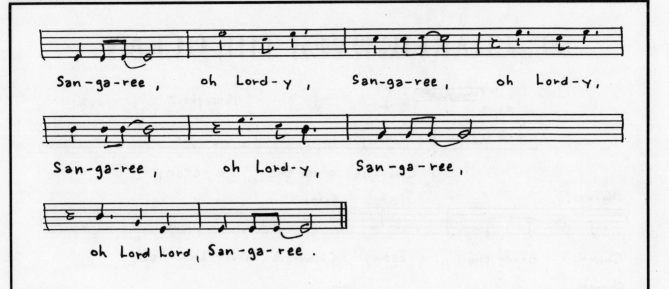

San-ga-ree, oh Lord-y, San-ga-ree, oh Lord-y,

San-ga-ree, oh Lord-y, San-ga-ree,

oh Lord Lord, San-ga-ree.

58. PEEP SQUIRREL

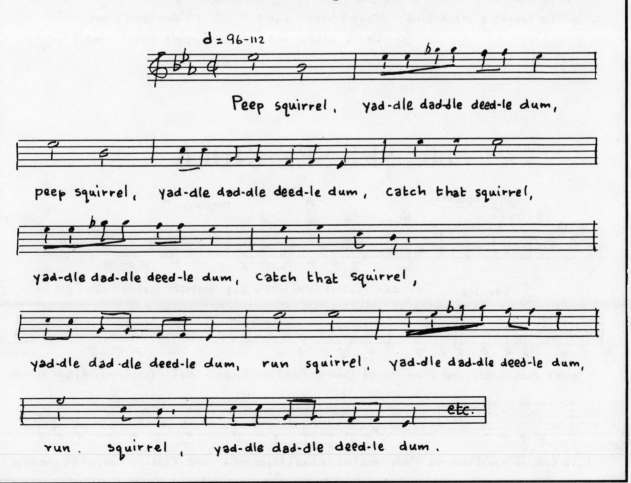

♩ = 96-112

Peep squirrel, yad-dle dad-dle deed-le dum,

peep squirrel, yad-dle dad-dle deed-le dum, catch that squirrel,

yad-dle dad-dle deed-le dum, catch that squirrel,

yad-dle dad-dle deed-le dum, run squirrel, yad-dle dad-dle deed-le dum,

run squirrel, yad-dle dad-dle deed-le dum.

59. CHARLIE OVER THE OCEAN

Char-lie o-ver the o-cean,

Chorus: / Solo:

Char-lie o-ver the o-cean, Char-lie o-ver the sea,

Chorus: / Solo:

Char-lie o-ver the sea, Char-lie caught a black-bird [or black-fish]

Chorus: / Solo: / Chorus:

Char-lie caught a black-bird, Might been me, Might been me.
[or: Can't catch me, Can't catch me.]

60. SEE SEE RIDER

See see ri-der (sat-is-fied) what's the mat-ter (sat-is-fied) I got to

work (sat-is-fied) and I am tired (sat-is-fied) and I can't eat (sat-is-fied) sat-is-fied

Lord (sat-is-fied) Mam-ma Mam-ma (sat-is-fied) leave me a-lone (sat-is-fied) when you were

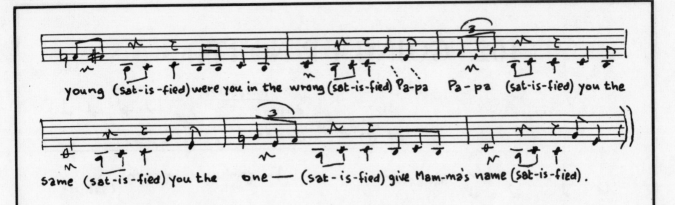

young (sat-is-fied) were you in the wrong (sat-is-fied) Pa-pa   Pa-pa   (sat-is-fied) you the

same (sat-is-fied) you the   one — (sat-is-fied) give Mam-ma's name (sat-is-fied).

61. BLUEBIRD BLUEBIRD

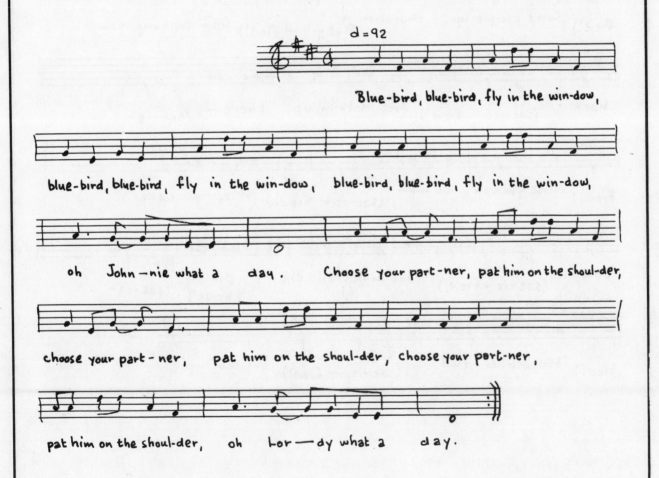

Blue-bird, blue-bird, fly in the win-dow,

blue-bird, blue-bird, fly in the win-dow,   blue-bird, blue-bird, fly in the win-dow,

oh   John—nie what a   day.   Choose your part-ner, pat him on the shoul-der,

choose your part-ner,   pat him on the shoul-der, choose your part-ner,

pat him on the shoul-der,   oh   Lor—dy what a   day.

62. GOING UP NORTH

63. LITTLE SALLY WALKER

Little Sal-ly Walk-er

sit-tin' in a sauc-er cry— in' for the old man to come for the dol-lar.

Ride Sal-ly ride, put your hands on your hips, ah let your back-bone slip, ah

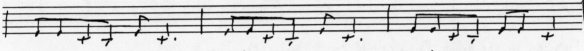

shake it to the east, ah shake it to the west, ah shake it to the ver-y one

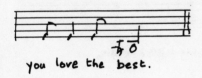

you love the best.

64. OLD LADY SALLY WANTS TO JUMP

Old la-dy Sal-ly wants to

jump-ty jump, jump-ty jump, jump-ty jump,

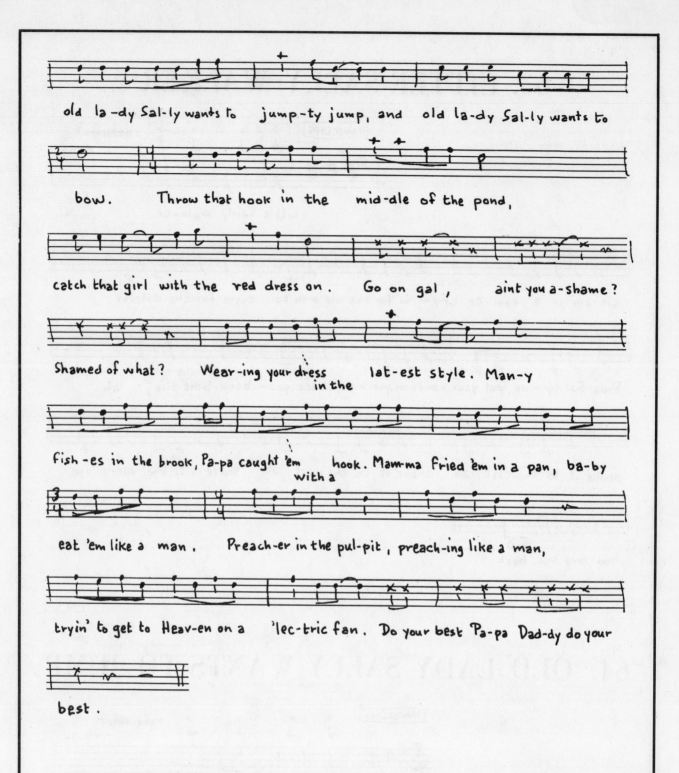

old la-dy Sal-ly wants to jump-ty jump, and old la-dy Sal-ly wants to

bow. Throw that hook in the mid-dle of the pond,

catch that girl with the red dress on. Go on gal, aint you a-shame?

Shamed of what? Wear-ing your dress in the lat-est style. Man-y

fish-es in the brook, Pa-pa caught 'em with a hook. Mam-ma fried 'em in a pan, ba-by

eat 'em like a man. Preach-er in the pul-pit, preach-ing like a man,

tryin' to get to Heav-en on a 'lec-tric fan. Do your best Pa-pa Dad-dy do your

best.

65 STOOPING ON THE WINDOW

66. BOB-A-NEEDLE

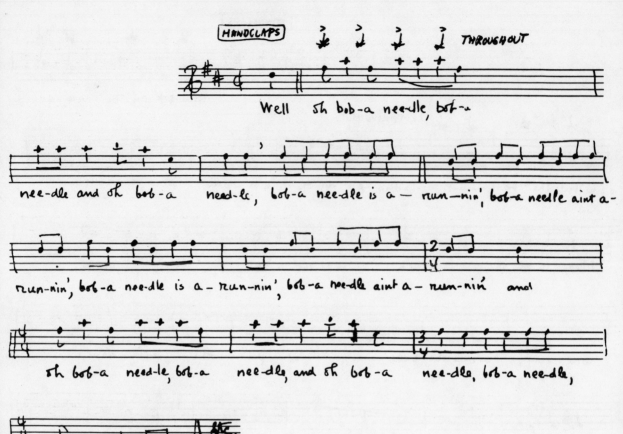

Well oh bob-a nee-dle, bob-a
nee-dle and oh bob-a need-le, bob-a needle is a — run—nin', bob-a needle aint a—
run-nin', bob-a nee-dle is a—run-nin', bob-a nee-dle aint a—run-nin' and
oh bob-a need-le, bob-a nee-dle, and oh bob-a nee-dle, bob-a nee-dle,
you got— bob-a.

67. ROSIE GAL

Ro-sie Rosie Rosie Ro-sie gal,

Ho - oh Ro-sie. Ro-sie gal and a Ro-sie gal—,

ho - oh Ro—sie, Ro-sie gal is a migh-ty prett-y gal,

ho - oh Ro-sie. Ro-sie gal is a migh-ty pet-ty gal,

ho - oh Ro-sie, I'm tal-kin' 'bout Ro-sie, Ro-sie gal,

ho - oh Ro- sie. I'm tal-kin' 'bout Ro-sie, Ro-sie gal—